EXMOOR
DARK SKIES

Our Window into a Universe of Fragile Starlight

SEB JAY

First published in Great Britain in 2014

Copyright © Seb Jay 2014

British Library Cataloguing-in-Publication Data
A CIP record for this title is available from the British Library.

ISBN 978 0 85710 091 7

PiXZ Books
Halsgrove House, Ryelands Business Park, Bagley Road, Wellington, Somerset TA21 9PZ
Tel: 01823 653777
Fax: 01823 216796
email: sales@halsgrove.com

An imprint of Halstar Ltd, part of the Halsgrove group of companies
Information on all Halsgrove titles is available at: www.halsgrove.com

Printed and bound in China by Everbest Printing Co Ltd

EXMOOR
NATIONAL PARK
Partnership Fund

With financial support from the Exmoor National Park Partnership Fund

Front cover:
Stag photograph
by Ray Stoneman

Dunkery Beacon
looking northwest

Contents

FIGHTING MY WAY up the stony path on the side of Dunkery Hill, a small telescope tube strapped to my back and tripod in hand, I was beginning to think that I had made a mistake. My gear was heavy; each lurch forward pained my thighs and made me wish that I'd chosen somewhere a little easier to enjoy an evening under Exmoor's starry skies.

That after all was my goal. A little bit of pre-trip internet digging on the Exmoor National Park website revealed the summit of Dunkery Hill to be the highest point on Exmoor at 520m above sea level. I was promised uninterrupted views of the horizon from one of the darkest places in Europe – a perfect antidote to the built-up light-polluted dirge from my home town location some 200 miles away to the northeast.

Here, where I stood, the air was clean. The sky glowed a deep indigo above my head, ushering in the dusky hues of a still evening twilight. For sure there was a nip in the September air, but with the Sun now lost below the horizon for the next 10 hours, and with a crescent moon setting in the west I was buzzing with excitement at the prospect of a journey into the depths of space and time from inside Exmoor's International Dark Sky Reserve on what promised to be a very dark night.

In the end the slow trek up the gently inclined 800-metre hillside track from Dunkery Gate Car Park was not too horrific. Once

Opposite:
Star Trails over
Wimbleball Lake.
Mark Holland

Left: A view from
Dunkery Hill.
Marilyn Peddle

The Devil's Punchbowl Exmoor.
Claudia Gabriela Marques

darkness fell my sky filled with starlight from thousands of naked eye stars. The Milky Way sprawled overhead, replete with glowing stellar clouds and dark rifts, while distant galaxies popped into view as clearly as I have ever seen them. I was like a child at Christmas, grinning from ear to ear at the magnificence of it all. It really did bring home to me what a special and rare resource Exmoor's dark sky is; a tiny window above our heads for us to peer into a vast exotic Universe of distant fragile light that can only be seen because of Exmoor's zero tolerance towards light pollution.

For most of us who live in urban and semi-urban settings our neighbouring streetlamps drown out the stars. They wash the night sky a grey-orange glow, reducing contrast between our visible universe and the background darkness of space. Only a smattering of the brightest stars are seen, and when a telescope is turned to the heavens much of what is there appears faint and washed out.

In a dark sky area, where there are no street lights, things are different. The darkness of space is more intense here, increasing sky contrast so that more stars, and fainter stars, can be seen. Right across the Exmoor International Dark Sky Reserve a moonless night sees the sky explode with starlight. Familiar constellations are overcrowded with stars that are invisible to the naked eye from a town or city. They seem to shine more brightly, and with greater vibrancy; and among them occasional delicate smudges of light are seen, marking out the locations of the brightest star clusters and galaxies cast upon Exmoor's inky black sky. Just looking up with your eyes here really is an awe-inspiring experience.

With a telescope the views just get better! My evening at Dunkery Beacon served up tens of thousands of stars sprawled across the sky. Ancient star clusters were resolved into collections of sparkling gems, each a sun in its own right. The ghostly glow from

The difference between an urban site and a dark sky site is striking.
Jeremy Stanley

From a dark sky site with a telescope star clusters appear as diamonds against a dark velvet background.
Seb Jay

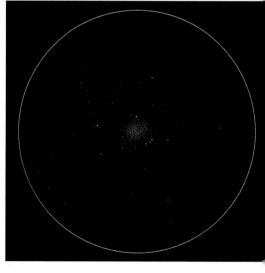

distant stellar nurseries, where new stars are being born, were captured at my eyepiece in high definition. Hundreds of galaxies, some with spiral arms snaking around dense white cores, revealed themselves large and bright. I even had the good fortune to pick out a faint comet with its tail sweeping back elegantly in its wake – something I would never have seen from my own back garden that evening. It certainly was an experience that I'll never forget – and all because Exmoor National Park Authority (ENPA) had the foresight to position this 267-square mile chunk of land in South West Britain as a dark sky area of international significance.

It was a journey that began in earnest for the ENPA in 2009. Inspired by a series of successful dark sky celebration events in support of the United Nations-endorsed International Year of Astronomy a commitment was made by the Park to promote the awareness and enjoyment of Exmoor as a dark sky area, while at the same time resolve to preserve and enhance the quality of the night sky. Two years later, and after a lot of hard work by the Dark Sky Development Team at ENPA, the International Dark Sky Association designated Exmoor National Park as Europe's first International Dark Sky Reserve. The Award was made as official recognition that Exmoor's night sky is one of the darkest in the World, and since then, ENPA its supporters, tourism providers, businesses and local communities across Exmoor have undertaken to keep it that way.

In writing *Exmoor Dark Skies* I hope to support this fantastic commitment. The intention is to bring Exmoor's night sky treasures to the attention of a wider audience, and to help keep that window into our Universe firmly open for future generations, free from the spectre of light pollution.

Whether you're an experienced amateur astronomer, new to the night sky, or simply want to learn more about the opportunities to stargaze from Exmoor, let this book serve as your local guide. It is packed with practical advice to help you get the most out of your dark sky adventure. In it you'll discover

* The best places on Exmoor to view the night sky
* How to navigate your way around the night sky with our maps and charts
* Which planets in our solar system you can see and when to look for them on Exmoor
* Deep sky treasures visible only with binoculars and telescopes
* Where to find the death masks of burnt out stars
* Ancient star clusters that you can see tonight that are older than the Earth itself
* Distant galaxies in deep space that you can see with a small telescope
* Some of the Universe's most exotic phenomena like supernova and quasars

So fasten your seatbelts and let me take you on a journey into the Universe. We'll move out from Exmoor up into Earth's atmosphere and out towards the planets, before accelerating through time and space to discover the most distant objects visible in the night sky from Exmoor. For each object we come across on the journey I'll provide details of how easy that object is to see, when to see it, how to see it and how to photograph it.

What will you find in the starlit skies above Exmoor when you look up tonight? A whole Universe awaits your discovery. Welcome to the Exmoor International Dark Sky Reserve.

The view from
Dunkery Beacon
at night.
Adrian Cubitt -
ATV Productions Ltd

You Are Here
◉ The Earth

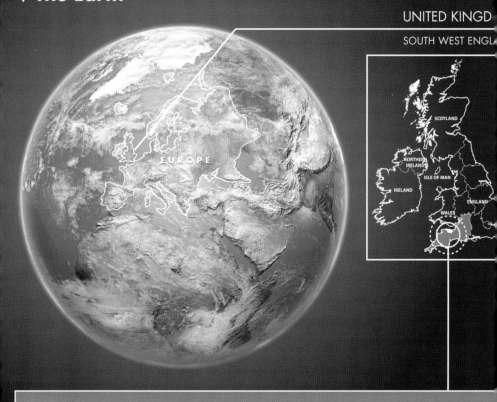

SCOTLAND

NORTHERN IRELAND

ISLE OF MAN

IRELAND

ENGLAND

WALES

EUROPE

EXMOOR NATIONAL PARK : INTERNATIONAL DARK SKY RESERVE

BRIDGEWAT

BAY

Lynmouth Countisbury
Martinhoe Lynton Brendon
Trentishoe Barbrook A39 Malmshead Culbone Porlock Selworthy Minehead
Berrynarbor West Lyn Oare Luccombe Watch
Combe Martin East Ilkerton Cheriton A39 Dunster
A3123 Parracombe Exmoor National Park Timberscombe Carhampt B3191 Old Cleev
East Down Kentisbury A39 EXMOOR Dunkery Washford Willit
Arlington A399 Challacombe FOREST Beacon Cutcombe Stogu
B3230 Loxhore B3358 Simonsbath Exford B3224 Luxborough Treborough
Shirwell Bratton Fleming Winsford BRENDON B32
Merwood Stoke Rivers Withypool Exton HILLS Brompton F
Pitton Goodleigh Charles B3223 Exton Upton Clatwo
Barnstaple Highbray Hawkridge A396 B3190
West Buckland Twitchen Brompton Regis Wivelis co
Swimbridge East Buckland Molland Dulverton Skilgate Chipstable
ishops Tawton Filleigh North Molton West Anstey B3222 Morebath Clayhanger
Chapelton A361 South Molton East Anstey Brushford
A377 Chittlehampton B3227 B3226 B3137 Bishops Nympton B3227 Knowstone
Umberleigh George Nympton

You Are Here

RISING UP FROM dramatic sea cliffs along the Bristol Channel coastline in South West England is Exmoor National Park. One of Britain's *breathing spaces* the Park is a 267-square mile area of open heathland, farmland and wild moor straddling the quieter parts of the counties of Somerset and Devon.

Deep flower-laden valleys and ancient woodlands crisscross this upland landscape; the River Exe has its source up in these hills, while the Devonian sandstone slates and shales through which the Exe carves its south-easterly path towards the sea are 390 - 360 million years old. It's a timescale worth bearing in mind, as you'll see later on!

Enriching Exmoor's ancient landscape are tales of romance, mystery and horror. *Lorna Doone: A Romance of Exmoor* by Richard Doddridge Blackmore is forever bound to the idyllic hamlet of Malmsmead. Stories of the Devil and pixies abound, while up on the desolate moors the scourge of Exmoor's farmers, the *Beast of Exmoor*, is said to still roam. No confirmed sightings of the Beast, presumed to be a large cat, were ever made. But to this day it is still held to blame for mysterious and unexplained occurrences on the Moor – like people carrying large telescope tubes across the dusk-lit landscape to look at the stars!

Exmoor's International Dark Sky Reserve is coterminous with the Exmoor National Park's boundary. Its darkest skies are in the central northern area of the Park – a 37.95-square mile core dark sky zone of open rural land that stretches from Wootton Courtenay in the east to just outside Parracombe in the west, taking in Luccombe, Horner, Exford, Simonsbath, Challacombe, Dunkery Hill, Brendon Common and Exmoor Forest in between. It is this core dark sky area that Exmoor National Park Authority is working hardest to protect from light pollution. An appraisal of Exmoor National Park's recommended stargazing sites are found towards the back of this book.

Opposite:
Exmoor National Park straddles the counties of Somerset and Devon in South West England. It is the first National Park in the UK to have International Dark Sky Reserve status, and the first location in Europe to have been designated a Dark Sky Reserve.
Hannah Collier

Overleaf:
Dunster Castle at night.
Adrian Cubitt - ATV Productions Ltd

In 2011 the International Dark Sky Association designated Exmoor National Park as a Silver Tier Dark Sky Reserve. In numbers this means that the background sky brightness in the core dark sky area as measured using the Unihedron Sky Quality Meter-L (SQM-L) method is greater than 21 magnitudes per square arc second. Many individual sites across Exmoor's core dark sky area in fact have recorded SQM-L readings higher than 21.4. That's dark enough to see sharp detail and dark rifts in the Milky Way, close on 5000 individual stars and at least two distant galaxies up to 2.9 million light years away from us – and all by just looking up into the sky with our eyes.

Outside the core dark sky area and out across the rest of Exmoor
National Park the night sky, while not being as intensely dark as

in the Atmosphere

in the Atmosphere

Noctilucent Clouds

The deep twilight of a mid-summer night above the wilds of Exmoor is where our astronomical journey begins with what is essentially an atmospheric phenomenon. At more than twice the height of Felix Baumgartner's 2012 Space Jump we find ourselves in the upper reaches of the mesosphere. It's a hostile environment; the temperature here some 80kms above Exmoor National Park gets down to an extremely cold -160°c. Atmospheric pressure is a fraction of what we're used to on terra firma. All in all, perfect conditions for noctilucent cloud formation.

Viewing Challenge:
Easy to see
Equipment: Eyes/Binoculars
Event Frequency: Occasional
Best Views: 10pm – 2am
mid May to Mid August.
Photography Tips: Tripod
mounted camera. 2-sec to
10-sec exposures at
moderate to high ISO.

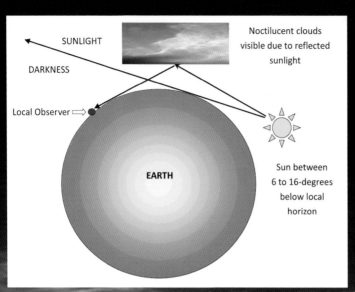

SUNLIGHT

DARKNESS

Local Observer

EARTH

Noctilucent clouds visible due to reflected sunlight

Sun between 6 to 16-degrees below local horizon

The only reason we see noctilucent clouds is that they are high enough in the atmosphere to reflect sunlight when the sky around the local observer is in darkness.

Noctilucent clouds are eerie cirrus cloud-like displays. They often appear blue or blue-green in colour and show delicate wave and herringbone patterns in their structure. The clouds are comprised of millions upon millions of extremely small ice crystals no larger than 0.1 microns in diameter, which shine intensely by reflected sunlight. They only appear on summer nights, between mid-May and mid-August, when the Sun is between 6° and 16° below Exmoor's northern horizon. Look for them between 10pm and 2am towards the north, especially if you're on Exmoor in the few weeks either side of the northern hemisphere's summer solstice.

Meteors

The real astronomical action begins in the thermosphere layer of our atmosphere, a few kilometres above where noctilucent clouds form. Here the temperature, astonishingly, climbs to above 1,000°c. That's hot enough to burn up incoming space debris to create those rapid bright trails of light that we know as meteors or shooting stars.

Every time a comet visits our part of the solar system it leaves behind a debris path of mineral dust, ice and rock in its wake. If the path the comet takes happens to intersect Earth's orbital path around the Sun, then at some point in the year our planet pushes through that debris path. When it does we get a meteor shower.

A bright meteor streaks through the sky in less than a couple of seconds. Mike Lewinski

The Perseids meteor shower, which peaks every year on August 12th – 13th with a rate of more than 80 meteors per hour, is caused by the debris path of Comet Swift-Tuttle. Debris from the more famous Halley's Comet spawns the less profuse Eta Aquarids meteor shower. This one peaks every 5 May with a rate of between 30 and 40 meteors per hour.

Larger pieces of debris sometimes burn up spectacularly as bright fireballs. Others occasionally penetrate into the lower atmosphere, exploding into fragments as the object encounters ever-higher atmospheric pressures, such as happened above Chelyabinsk in Russia in February 2013. Fragments that do make landfall are called meteorites.

Viewing Challenge:
Easy to see
Equipment: Eyes / Binoculars
Event Frequency: Often
Best Views: On peak nights of meteor showers.
Photography Tips: Tripod mounted camera. Continuous 20-sec exposures at high ISO on peak nights. Use a wide angle lens.

Meteor Showers

SHOWER	DATES	PEAK	MAX. RATE / HR	RADIANT CONSTELLATION
Quadrantids	Jan 1-6	Jan 3	40-60	Bootes
Lyrids	Apr 19-25	Apr 21	20-25	Lyra
Eta Aquarids	May 1-10	May 6	15-20	Aquarius
Delta Aquarids	Jul 15-Aug 15	Jul 29	15-20	Aquarius
Perseids	Jul 23-Aug 20	Aug 12	70-90	Perseus
Draconids	Oct 6-10	Oct 8	5-10	Draco
Orionids	Oct 16-27	Oct 21	10-25	Orion
Taurids	Oct 20-Nov 30	Nov 5	5-10	Taurus
Leonids	Nov 15-20	Nov 17	10-20	Leo
Geminids	Dec 7-15	Dec 13	50-70	Gemini
Ursids	Dec 17-25	Dec 22	5-10	Ursa Minor

Annual Meteor Showers.

Aurora Borealis (Northern Lights)

Put away your passport. Cancel that trip to the Arctic Circle. You can see the Northern Lights from Exmoor! Okay, granted, you won't get to see them very often from South West England. In fact they are a very rare sight indeed. Using data from the British Astronomical Association we can deduce that in any one year there are likely to be only around five nights on which the aurora borealis is visible from Exmoor. Some years there'll be more displays, some years less. Much depends on the state of that giant ball of gas in the sky that we know as the Sun.

Being a complex sphere the Sun always rotates faster at its equator than at its poles. This rotation disparity twists and distorts the Sun's powerful magnetic field lines, loops of which poke up through the visible surface of the Sun as dark cool sunspots. The greater the rotation disparity, the more twisted the magnetic field

Viewing Challenge:
Easy to see
Equipment: Eyes/Binoculars
Event Frequency: Rare
Best Views: At the peak of each 11-year solar cycle.
Photography Tips: Tripod mounted camera. 20-sec to 30-sec exposures at moderate ISO. Use a wide angle lens.

Glowing green, red and purple auroral rays can shift, change shape and even pulsate through an intense display. Guido da Rozze

lines become, and so the more sunspots there are on the Sun. When the Sun's magnetic field lines become ultra-distorted they stretch and snap releasing huge amounts of energy across the electromagnetic spectrum as solar storms.

If a solar storm pushes off in the direction of Earth it interacts with our planet's magnetic field. Incoming protons and electrons in the solar storm material collide with atoms and molecules of nitrogen and oxygen in our upper atmosphere. This is what causes the aurorae. What we see are green arcs and curtains of light, glowing green and red rayed bands and even pulsing patches of ghostly red and purple light invading Exmoor's sky from the north.

Opposite: Some of the most spectacular night sky phenomena occur in Earth's upper atmosphere. Hannah Collier.

It is an incredible sight. But the Sun needs to be hyperactive and throwing off regular solar storms in our direction for us to have a chance of seeing such a display from Exmoor. An eleven-year cycle is at play here with magnetic activity increasing to a peak and then dipping back down to a minimum. The last peak in activity was in 2013 – and it was a weak peak with very few solar storms. The next peak is due in 2023 / 2024, so we might have to wait a while yet to see the northern lights from Exmoor.

Earth's Atmosphere
Height of NLC, Aurora & Meteors

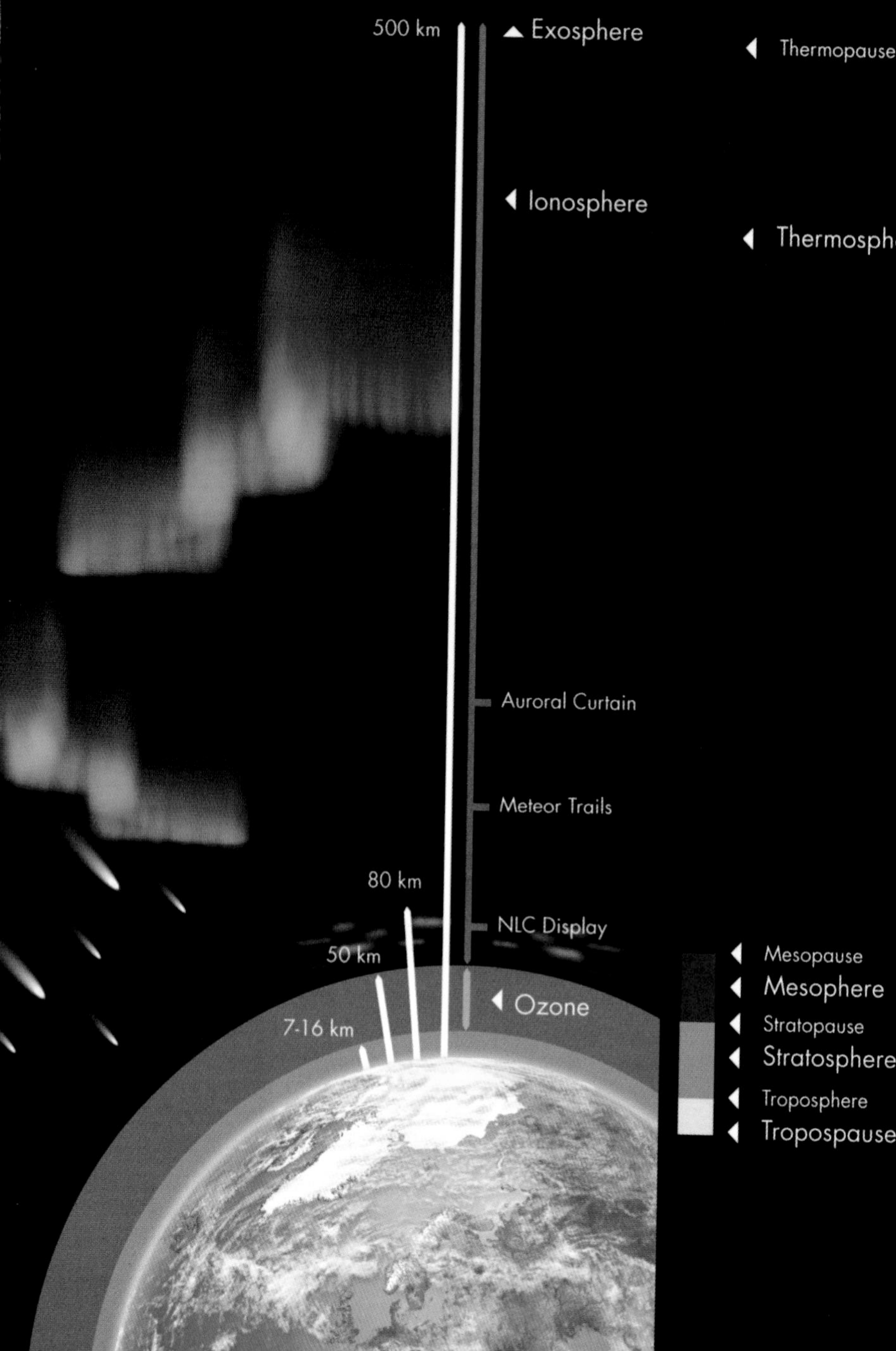

500 km — ▲ Exosphere

◀ Thermopause

◀ Ionosphere

◀ Thermosph

Auroral Curtain

Meteor Trails

80 km — NLC Display

50 km

◀ Ozone

7-16 km

◀ Mesopause
◀ Mesosphere
◀ Stratopause
◀ Stratosphere
◀ Troposphere
◀ Tropospause

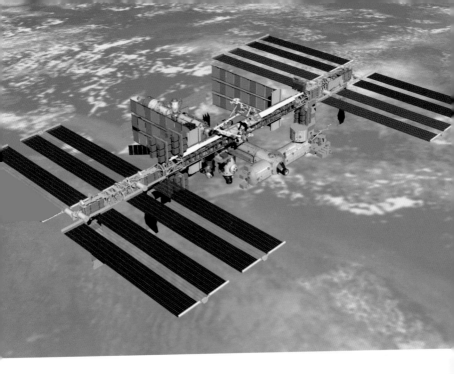

In Orbit

International Space Station (ISS)

Freefalling around the Earth at 17,500mph some 250 miles up above our heads is the farthest human outpost from Exmoor – the International Space Station (ISS). Continuously occupied since 31st October 2000 the ISS has been home to more than 200 astronauts. A crew of six stay on-board for several months at a time occupying a living space that is comparable to that of a five bedroom house. During their time on the ISS the crew clock up 160 hours of labour per week between them, working on everything from microgravity experiments to space station repairs.

Watching this quiet sentinel of the sky sail overhead from the ground is an awe-inspiring experience. It appears as a bright beacon of white light moving steadily eastwards. It always rises in the west or southwest and sets towards the east or southeast. Sometimes the ISS passes directly overhead, taking almost ten minutes to cross the sky giving you plenty of time to view it and

ng Challenge:
o see
ment: Eyes / Binoculars
cope
Frequency: Often
Views: When the ISS
duled to pass almost
ly overhead as seen
Exmoor.
ography Tips: Tripod
ted camera. 15-sec+
ures at moderate to
SO.

to photograph it. You can even watch it in binoculars or a telescope, although tracking such a quick moving object isn't without its challenges!

A good quality 90mm refractor is all that is needed to reveal the basic structure of the ISS from Exmoor. You'll see it as a capital 'H' shape, its central module flanked by sets of solar panels. Larger telescopes yield more detail on the space station. You can even make out docked spacecraft modules with telescopes of 250mm aperture. Not a bad result when you consider that you're looking at an object no bigger than 100 metres long from a distance of more than 250 miles away!

The ISS orbits the Earth once every ninety minutes. It rarely follows the same path so each pass takes a different line across the sky. If you have a smartphone then you'll have a number of apps available to you that you can use to get information on when and where to look to see the next ISS pass for your location. Websites like http://www.heavens-above.com also provide this information once you've plugged in your latitude and longitude.

Opposite: The 16-strong array of solar panels on the International Space Station can easily be seen from Exmoor using a 150mm telescope. NASA

Photographing the ISS from the ground is easy. This basic shot of the ISS sweeping through the top part of the Summer Triangle is a 15-second exposure taken using a Canon compact digital camera with fixed lens at ISO 800. Seb Jay

Sunlight reflecting off any one of the three metal panels on an Iridium satellite is the cause of an Iridium flare in the night sky.
Flickr / Wikipedia

Satellites and Iridium Flares

Circling the Earth right now, up to a height of 500 miles above Exmoor, are more than 20,000 visible man-made satellites and pieces of man-made space debris. Everything from active GPS and telecommunication satellites to science research platforms, military spy hardware, dead spacecraft and spent rocket boosters from 1960s' space launches can be seen silently sailing overhead on a clear night.

For the most part you only need look up at the sky in the right place at the right time to see one or more of them. Many are naked eye visibility as sunlight glints off their reflective bodies, making them appear as a constantly moving light in the sky visible for several minutes at a time. Even spacecraft parts as small as 3m x 2m reflect sunlight with enough intensity for them to be seen from Exmoor without binoculars or a telescope.

With optical aid more and fainter orbiting objects can be tracked. You can even seek out satellites with geostationary orbits. These are satellites that, from Earth, appear to remain fixed against the background stars as their orbits match Earth's rotational speed.

Part of the fun of satellite watching is working out what you're looking at. A number of organisations maintain satellite information and tracking databases. Websites such as heavens-above.com provide information on orbital paths, visibility timings, brightness and a graphic of the satellite's track against the constellations as seen from your local observing site. What type of satellites might you see tonight?

Iridium Flares
In the late 1990s, just as mobile phones were gaining global popularity, Iridium LLC in the U.S. began launching the Iridium Satellite Constellation – a fleet of telecommunication satellites intended to provide satellite phone services from any point on Earth. The company went bankrupt in 1999 and the business sold off to investors at a fraction of the $5 billion project cost.

Today some 66 active Iridium satellites orbit Earth under new owners Iridium Satellite LLC. The U.S. military is one of their largest customers, and the corporation plan to launch a new satellite fleet from 2015.

For skywatchers Iridium satellites really put on a great light show. Thanks to their construction each Iridium satellite has three door-sized antennae that maintain an oblique angle to the Earth's surface for data transmissions. These antennae are highly reflective and occasionally catch the sunlight, lighting up the sky momentarily as a two – four second flare of light brighter than Venus appears in the night sky.

It's a spectacular sight, and with precise orbital data for the fleet freely available online it is easy to forecast when and where the next flare can be seen.

> **Viewing Challenge:** Easy to see
> **Equipment**: Eyes / Binoculars / Telescope
> **Event Frequency:** Very often
> **Best Views:** April to September
> **Photography Tips:** Tripod mounted camera. 30-sec+ exposures at moderate to high ISO.

HUBBLE SPACE TELESCOPE
10 DECEMBER 2013
19:05 - 19:12

CASSIOPEIA
PERSEUS
19:09 — 310 Degrees NW
19:05
19:11   19:10   CYGNUS
ANDROMEDA
PEGASUS
TAURUS   ARIES
19:12
ORION
W
E
GROUND

Iconic spacecraft in orbit around the Earth can be tracked across Exmoor's night sky if you know where to look. This is the path the Hubble Space Telescope took on 10 December 2013. It is visible from Exmoor with the naked eye many times through the course of the year.

23

The full moon as it appears through a 200mm aperture telescope at x63 magnification.
Seb Jay

The Moon

ORBITING EARTH AT an average distance of 384,400kms is a familiar sight – the Moon. The Greek philosopher Anaxagoras (500BC - 428BC) was the first to correctly propose that the Moon's light is reflected sunlight. It was not until the invention of the telescope however that the Moon was proved not to be a smooth surface, but is instead strewn with deep craters and high mountain chains. The actual geological composition of the Moon is a relatively recent discovery, only being confirmed in the twentieth century by spacecraft landers and orbiters.

Formation

Current theory asserts that the Moon formed around 4.5 billion years ago when an object about 10 per cent the mass of the Earth collided with our newly formed planet. At that time Earth was still an extremely young seething molten mass of material. The collision

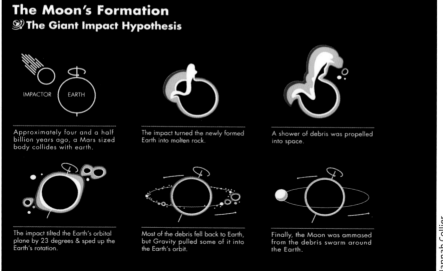

The Moon's Formation
☽ **The Giant Impact Hypothesis**

Approximately four and a half billion years ago, a Mars sized body collides with earth.

The impact turned the newly formed Earth into molten rock.

A shower of debris was propelled into space.

The impact tilted the Earth's orbital plane by 23 degrees & sped up the Earth's rotation.

Most of the debris fell back to Earth, but Gravity pulled some of it into the Earth's orbit.

Finally, the Moon was ammased from the debris swarm around the Earth.

Hannah Collier

lifted a giant dollop of this material off the Earth and into orbit, where it eventually coalesced and cooled to give us our Moon.

The first two billion years of the Moon's life were pretty turbulent. Giant space rocks rained down on the lunar surface, just as they did on Earth – a by-product of our solar system's formation. As the Moon cooled active volcanoes spewed magma out across the Moon's hardening crust forming huge glowing seas of lava. Because there is no atmosphere or weather on the Moon all of these formation scars are perfectly preserved to this day.

Orbit

The Moon orbits the Earth once every 27.32 days. This is known as a *sidereal month*. But because the Earth is moving in its own orbit around the Sun it actually takes the Moon 29.53 days to reach the same relative position as at which it started. This is called a *synodic month*, and it is for this reason that the date of a Full Moon only ever regresses by a night or two in any given calendar month.

If you've ever looked at the Moon you'll know that we always see the same side of the Moon's surface and never the far side. This is because the Moon takes the same amount of time to rotate on its axis as it takes to orbit the Earth, and so always presents the same face to us. The Moon therefore is said to be in synchronous rotation with Earth.

Biggest and smallest full moons.

Biggest and Smallest Full Moons

PERIGEE 'SUPERMOONS'	DISTANCE	APOGEE 'MICROMOONS'	DISTANCE
August 10th 2014	356,896km	January 16th 2014	406,536km
September 25th 2015	356,867km	March 5th 2015	406,385km
November 14th 2016	356,511km	April 21st 2016	406,350km
January 1st 2018	356,565km	June 8th 2017	406,401km
February 19th 2019	356,761km	July 27th 2018	406,222km
April 7th 2020	356,908km	September 13th 2019	406,377km
May 26th 2021	357,309km	October 30th 2020	406,392km
July 13th 2022	357,263km	December 18th 2021	406,321km
August 30th 2023	357,181km	February 5th 2023	406,475km
October 17th 2024	357,172km	February 24th 2024	406,314km

October 28, 2012
Distance: 400,000 km

June 21, 2013
Distance: 364,000 km

Another interesting aspect of the Moon's orbit is that it does not follow a circular path around the Earth. Instead the Moon follows an elliptical orbit. Through the course of a month it gradually drifts closer to the Earth and then further away. When the Moon is at its closest point in its orbit to Earth it is called a perigee moon. When that point coincides with a full moon we call it a supermoon, and it can be as close as 356,400kms to our planet. At its furthest the Moon is said to be at apogee. Apogee moons can be as distant as 406,700kms from Earth and appear up to 12% smaller than at perigee. The difference in Moon size as seen from Exmoor is apparent if you photograph it at full moon using the same equipment at apogee and perigee.

The difference between a supermoon and a micromoon is best seen when they are put side by side.
David R. Carroll

Phases

Most of us are familiar with the phases of the Moon, but perhaps not so familiar with the celestial mechanics behind it. To understand why we see different amounts of the Moon's Earth-facing hemisphere illuminated we must first get to grips with the relationship between the Earth, the Moon and the Sun through the course of a lunar orbit.

When the Moon sits directly between the Earth and the Sun we cannot see it from Exmoor or from anywhere else on Earth. From

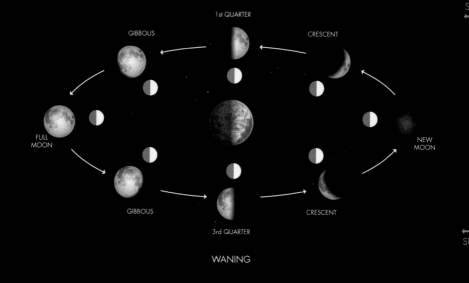

WANING

The Lunar Cycle as
seen from Earth.
Hannah Collier

our viewpoint the Moon is close to the Sun in the daytime sky, and
so the Sun's glare drowns it out. Normally the Moon passes above
or below the Sun's disc in the sky marking the start of a lunar
month – a new moon. Occasionally the path the Moon takes in its
orbit means it passes directly in front of the Sun causing a solar
eclipse.

Just as the Earth orbits the Sun in an anti-clockwise motion so the
Moon also orbits the Earth anti-clockwise. A couple of days after new
moon our only natural satellite will have moved far enough around
in its orbit to appear as a thin waxing crescent in the early evening
sky shortly after sunset. The reason we see it only as a thin crescent
is because most of the Moon's visible hemisphere is still pointing
away from the Sun, with the sun's light just catching a small portion
of the right-hand side of the Moon's disc as we see it.

Further into the Moon's orbit more and more of the lunar surface
moves into sunlight. At the quarter way orbit point the Moon
appears half lit – dark on the left, illuminated on the right, and
is visible in the evening sky for a few hours after sundown. By

the time it is opposite the Sun in its orbit, the Earth sitting directly between the two, we get our full moon. Being opposite the Sun it appears in our night-time sky in the east at around sunset, and sets in the west at around sunrise. Sometimes the path the Moon takes in its orbit when full places it directly in the shadow cast from Earth by the Sun. When this happens we get a lunar eclipse.

After full moon we move into the second half of the lunar month. The illumination process we saw between new moon and full moon happens again, but in reverse. Darkness encroaches from the right side of the lunar disc this time as the Moon wanes. At the three-quarter way orbit point half of the Moon is once again lit – the left side in sunlight and the right side in shadow. By now the Moon is rising over Exmoor in the early hours of the morning, and can be seen setting in the west in the daytime sky.

Towards the end of the lunar cycle the Moon appears as a thin waning crescent rising in the dawn sky just ahead of the Sun in the east. Gradually it moves closer to the Sun from our viewing perspective, drawing the lunar month to a close, and the start of the process again with a new moon.

Surface Features

Turn a pair of binoculars to the Moon and you'll be greeted with a close-up view of its larger scale surface features. With a telescope you'll be able to see a lot more. A reflector with a 150mm primary mirror for example will resolve craters on the moon that are as small as 2.5km in diameter.

Maria
Those dark patches on the lunar surface that help to make up the grinning 'Man in the Moon' pattern are called *Maria* – Latin for 'Seas'. Each *Mare* or 'Sea' is a huge impact basin that filled with enormous volumes of glowing basaltic lava from volcanic eruptions some three – four billion years ago. Today we see the Maria filled with the solidified smooth basalt rocks left behind as the lava cooled. *Mare Imbrium* (the Sea of Rains), located in the Moon's northwest quadrant, is the largest impact basin on the lunar surface measuring 1123km across. The first lunar landing involving Apollo 11 took place on the shores of another *Mare* – *Mare Tranquillitatis* or the Sea of Tranquillity.

Viewing Challenge: Easy to see
Equipment: Eyes / Binoculars / Telescope
Best Views: All year round
Photography Tips: The easiest way to photograph the Moon through a telescope is to hold the camera up to the telescope's eyepiece and take the shot. Medium to high ISO recommended. Exposure range is 1/125s for a thin crescent moon to 1/2500 for a full moon.

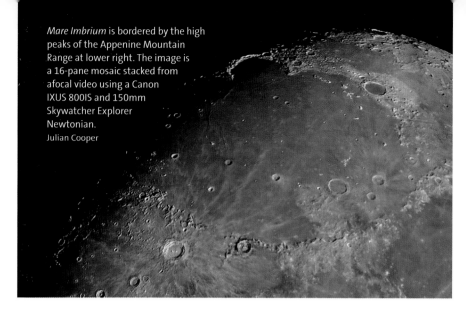

Mare Imbrium is bordered by the high peaks of the Appenine Mountain Range at lower right. The image is a 16-pane mosaic stacked from afocal video using a Canon IXUS 800IS and 150mm Skywatcher Explorer Newtonian.
Julian Cooper

Opposite, top left: Tycho Crater is perhaps the most recognisable crater on the Moon. It is located in the southern lunar highlands and is noteworthy for the distinctive bright rays that extend from it across the lunar surface for hundreds of kilometres. The mountain peak at the crater's centre is 1.6kms high.
Avani Soares

Opposite, top right: The Hortensius volcanic domes are highlighted by the yellow box right of centre. Upper left is the Milichius dome field. Avani Soares

Highlands

The brighter areas on the lunar surface are rocky hills, mountains and elevated plateaus. Much of these areas are overlain by impact craters creating a jumbled landscape of rough rocky terrain. One of the most impressive highland features through a small telescope is the Apennine Mountain Range – a chain of peaks up to 5kms high that curve gently around the southeastern boundary of *Mare Imbrium*. Apollo 15's landing site is close by.

Craters

Formed mainly by meteorite and asteroid impacts, craters are by far the most abundant type of surface feature visible on the lunar surface. Binoculars show many of the Moon's major craters, including *Tycho, Copernicus* and *Kepler* – three distinctive impact features with rays of bright material extending out from them. In a small telescope many thousands of craters are revealed in stunning detail. You can see the complex craggy structures that form the sidewalls of the craters, the crater's smooth floor and the mountain peaks that often dominate at the centre of many of the larger craters.

Valleys

Valleys on the Moon are called *Rilles*. Some are meandering channels gouged out of the lunar surface by fast-moving lava flows. Others form arcs and straight lines and have no confirmed origin. Telescopes of 150mm aperture and more reveal a number of lunar rilles, the longest of which is the 426km-long Rimae

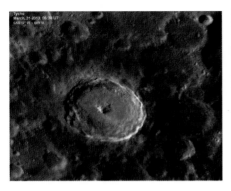

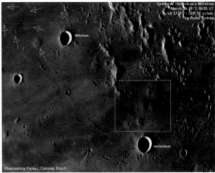

Sirsalis on the western limb of the Moon. It is best seen from full moon onwards using a high magnification eyepiece, and is easy to find slightly to the north of the dark oval Grimaldi Crater.

Volcanic Domes
Volcanic domes appear as small round bumps on the surface of the Moon. These long extinct lunar volcanoes normally occur in small groups and are pitted in their centres by caldera-style craters. One of the easiest dome groups to spot with a telescope is the Hortensius dome field. Look for a small collection of five to six bumps in the darker lunar surface a short way to the north of the Hortensius Crater. It is sandwiched almost centrally between the rayed craters of Copernicus and Kepler, and is best viewed when the waxing Moon is ten days old, or when the waning Moon is twenty-five days old. A high magnification eyepiece of x150 or x200 will yield a view of those caldera-like craters in the middle of the domes.

Sketch of Pythagoras Crater at the eyepiece of a 215mm reflector at x240 magnification. Seb Jay

Below: Crater structure and sinuous rilles are revealed in high definition through larger telescopes at high magnification. The Arzachel, Alphonsus, Ptolemaeus and Rupes Recta region. Teva Chene

Venus, the Moon and Jupiter all gathered in the western sky after sunset in February 2012.
Neal Simpson

3 Exploring the Inner Solar System

Our Closest Planetary Neighbours: Venus & Mars

Venus

VENTURING OUT into the solar system from our own Moon the next closest celestial object to us is the planet Venus. Shining bright enough to cast a shadow on the ground during the darkest of nights on Exmoor, Venus can get as close as 38 million kilometres to Earth in its orbit. Its immense brightness is down to the thick acidic clouds that blanket the Venusian disc. The clouds reflect as much as 70% of the sunlight reaching the planet, making it shine brightly. In fact Venus shines so brightly that it can sometimes be found in the daytime sky. You just need to know where to look!

Beneath its thick cloudy atmosphere Venus is a treacherous place. The surface temperature is above 450°c making it the hottest

Best times to see Venus from Exmoor.

Venus From Exmoor

VISIBLE	WHERE	CLOSE ENCOUNTERS
Feb-Jul 2014	Morning Sky Feb SE, Mar SE,Apr ESE, May E, Jun E, Jul E	Mercury - Jul 2014
Jan-Jul 2015	Evening Sky Jan SW, Feb SW, Mar WSW, Apr W, May W, Jun WNW, Jul W	Mercury - Jan 2015 Mars - Feb 2015 Jupiter - Jun 2015
Aug 2015-Feb 2016	Morning Sky Aug E, Sep, ESE, Oct SE, Nov SE, Dec SSE, Jan SSE	Mars - Sep 2015 Mars & Jupiter Oct/Nov 2015 Saturn - Jan 2016
Sep 2016-Mar 2017	Evening Sky Sep SW, Oct SW, Nov SSW, Dec SSW, Jan SSW, Feb SW, Mar WSW	Mars - Feb 2017

planet in our solar system. Its choking atmosphere is 96% carbon dioxide, while surface pressure is 90 times more than on Earth. Go here and you'll be burnt, choked and crushed all at the same time!

From our safe vantage point on Exmoor Venus is easiest seen shortly after sunset or just before sunrise. The planet spends its time alternating between several week-long spells in the evening sky and then the morning sky as it moves along its 224-day orbit around the Sun. Best visibility is when the planet reaches its greatest angular distance from the Sun in its orbit as seen from Earth (called greatest elongation), and when that point coincides with the steepest angle of the ecliptic to the local horizon – a configuration that only occurs during spring evenings and autumn mornings. *[The ecliptic is the path across the sky that the Sun and the planets appear to move on through the course of a year, and is equivalent to the solar system's orbital plane.]* It is at these times that Venus reaches its highest point above the horizon and is visible in darkness for several hours after sunset or before sunrise. Use the Venus Visibility table on page 33 to work out when and where to see Venus next.

Observing Venus

Stargazing locations with a good view to your west, south and east work best for observing Venus. Evening apparitions require a good view to the west and southwest; morning apparitions need that same good view to the east and southeast.

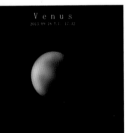

Venusian cloud features are more easily seen and photographed when a UV filter is used.

Stefano Quaresima

A 90mm telescope or larger will show Venus as a disc of light. It'll also show the changing phases of illumination as the planet waxes and wanes, much like the Moon, during the course of the Venusian orbit. When Venus is located between the Earth and the Sun, and so is closest to us, a pair of 10x50 binoculars is all you'll need to show the planet's phases.

Careful and systematic observations of Venus with larger telescopes provide access to other interesting Venusian phenomena. These include:

Cloud Detail – Subtle cloud structure showing light grey bands and patches as well as brighter spots and brighter polar cusps can sometimes be seen with the aid of colour filters and visual contrast filters.

Terminator Irregularity – The divide between the illuminated part of the disc and the dark side can show tonal variations across the transition area. Sometimes the terminator might appear quite flat or more prominently curved than appears natural.

Ashen Light – On very rare occasions the dark portion of the Venusian disc can appear faintly illuminated, more particularly when Venus is a narrow crescent. What causes this faint illumination is unknown.

With a camera or webcam attached to a modest telescope set-up amateur astronomers can produce highly detailed images of the Martian surface. Larry Summers

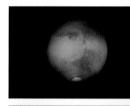

Mars

No other planet in our solar system garners as much popular attention as Mars. From epic tales of Martians attacking Earth to stories of futuristic Martian landscapes colonised by humans and aliens, the Red Planet has, for more than a century, served as a stage for our ponderings about our place in the Universe. It was only in the 1970s, when the Viking spacecraft landers photographed the Martian surface for the first time, that the real Martian story began to unfold. Today most of the Martian surface has been mapped in high resolution by a succession of orbiting spacecraft. The European Space Agency's Mars Express Orbiter alone has mapped around 90% of the surface in 3D. You can even roam around Mars from the comfort of your living room using the Google Mars Map!

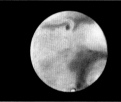

Mars reveals dark markings and bright limb hazes in telescopes of 150mm aperture. Sketch by Seb Jay

Best times to see Mars from Exmoor

Mars From Exmoor

VISIBLE MORNING SKY	VISIBLE EVENING SKY	OPPOSITION DATE	BEST VIEWS
Aug 2013 - Feb 2014	Feb 2014 - Feb 2015	April 8th 2014 (Virgo Constellation)	Feb-Jun 2014
Sep 2015 - Mar 2016	Mar 2016 - Apr 2017	May 22nd 2016 (Scorpio Constellation)	Mar-Jul 2016
Oct 2017 - Jul 2018	Jul 2018 - May 2019	July 27th 2018 (Capricorn Constellation)	Jun 2018-Jan 2019
Nov 2019 - Sep 2020	Sep 2020 - Jun 2021	October 13th 2020 (Pisces Constellation)	Aug 2020-Mar 2021

Adding significantly to our body of knowledge about the Red Planet over the past decade have been the three NASA rovers – Spirit, Opportunity and Curiosity. Their work has revealed a frozen desolate world, but a world that was once not so different to ours. Enormous amounts of surface water once flowed and pooled on the surface some 3 billion years ago. Evidence for drinkable water in the Martian past has also been found, and some scientists think that there may be frozen water reserves on Mars to this day, buried deep underground. Whether or not there is life on Mars now, or has been in the distant past, is a question that remains unanswered.

Observing Mars
Mars is easy to see with the naked eye for two – three months either side of the date of *opposition* (i.e. when the planet is opposite the Sun in the sky as we see it from Earth). Around opposition Mars is at its closest point to us in its 687-day orbit, and so is at its brightest and most obvious in Exmoor's dark skies. It'll appear as a bright crimson-orange point of light, although nowhere near rivalling the light of Venus. Use the Mars Visibility table to find out when and where to look for Mars next.

Dark markings on the Martian surface can be identified with the use of a Mars albedo map.
Ralph Aeschilman

With an equatorial diameter of 6,787kms Mars is almost half the size of Earth. It is too small to show any sort of disc in binoculars, and you need a telescope with at least a 90mm objective lens or

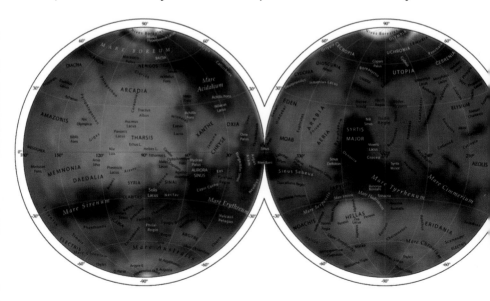

equivalent-sized primary mirror to start seeing detail on the surface. Larger telescopes offer bigger, brighter and more detailed views. Use magnifications of x200 or more on a night when the upper air is still. Most obvious will be the Martian polar cap – a distinct white slither of carbon dioxide ice sat over whichever pole is visible at the time. You might also get to see subtle dark markings over the planet's brown-orange surface. As Mars rotates about its tilted axis at a little over twenty-four hours you can watch the position of surface markings change, something that is very obvious over the course of two – three hours.

Other features to look out for include:

White Clouds – White clouds of carbon dioxide and trace amounts of water vapour commonly form in the thin cold Martian atmosphere close to the poles. They are also to be found high up above Mars's extinct volcanoes, and make Olympus Mons – the largest volcano in the solar system – easier to identify in a telescope.

Limb Frosts and Hazes – Mars's twenty-four-hour rotation period means that areas of the planet are constantly moving out of the darkness into sunlight on the eastern morning limb and back into darkness on the western evening limb. As they do so the temperature differential between night and day causes thin frosts and hazes to become visible as white patches close to both limbs.

Viewing Challenge: Easy to see. Surface detail is difficult to see
Equipment: Eyes / Binoculars / Telescope
Event Frequency: Occasional
Best Views: See Mars Visibility table.
Photography Tips: Mars is bright enough to image as a point of light with a camera and wide-angle lens. To capture detail on the planet a camera or webcam mounted on a telescope, which is itself fixed to a motorised equatorial mount works best. Resulting images can be stacked together in image processing software to obtain a high-detailed view.

Elusive Mercury

At a close-approach distance of 77 million kilometres to Exmoor, some two-hundred times further out than the Moon is from Earth, we find ourselves on planet Mercury – the innermost planet to the Sun in our solar system. It's a small inhospitable world. In sunlight we'd bake on this 3,000-mile wide rock in searing temperatures that can reach highs of 400°c. At night we'd freeze in lows of -184°c.

Mercury takes just eighty-eight days to complete an orbit of the Sun. It flits into the morning and evening skies with regularity through the year, but never rises very high above the horizon, rarely getting out of the twilight zone. As a consequence Mercury really only ever becomes visible from Exmoor for two – three weeks at a time at dusk in the western sky or at dawn in the eastern sky.

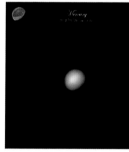

Mercury does not easily reveal its surface features.
Stefano Quaresima.

Mercury From Exmoor

EVENING	BEST VISIBILITY	COMPASS	MORNING	BEST VISIBILITY	COMPASS
May 2014	May 25th - 9:30pm	290-300°	Jul 2014	Jul 12th - 4am	060-065°
Jan 2015	Jan 14th - 5pm	225-230°	Oct/Nov 2014	Nov 1st - 6am	105-115°
May 2015	May 7th - 9pm	290-300°	Oct 2015	Oct 16th - 6am	090-100°
Dec 2015	Dec 29th - 4:30pm	220-225°	Feb 2016	Feb 7th - 7am	130-135°
Apr 2016	Apr 18th - 8:30pm	285-295°	Sep/Oct 2016	Sep 28th - 6am	085-095°
Mar/Apr 2017	Apr 1st - 8pm	275-280°	Jan 2017	Jan 19th - 7am	130-140°
Mar 2018	Mar 15th - 6:30pm	265-270°	Sep 2017	Sep 12th - 5:30am	075-085°
Jul 2018	Jul 12th - 10pm	290-295°	Dec 2017/Jan2018	Jan 1st - 7am	130-140°
Feb/Mar 2019	Feb 27th - 6:30pm	255-265°	Aug/Sep 2018	Aug 26th - 5am	070-075°
Jun 2019	Jun 23rd - 10pm	295-305°	Dec 2018	Dec 15th - 6:30am	125-135°
Feb 2020	Feb 10th - 5:30pm	245-250°	Aug 2019	Aug 9th - 4:30am	065-070°

Best times to see Mercury from Exmoor.

Viewing Challenge:
Quite challenging to see
Equipment: Eyes /
Binoculars / Telescope
Event Frequency: Occasional
Best Views: See Mercury
Visibility table.
Photography Tips: Mercury
is bright enough to image as a
point of light with a camera on
a tripod at dusk or dawn. To
capture detail on the planet a
camera or webcam mounted
on a telescope, which is itself
fixed to a motorised equatorial mount works best.
Resulting images can be
stacked together in image
processing software to obtain
a high-detailed view.

As with Venus, by far the best time to catch elusive Mercury is when the planet reaches its greatest elongation, and when that point coincides with the steepest angle of the ecliptic to the local horizon. It is at these times that Mercury reaches its highest points above the horizon, and is therefore easier to seek out with binoculars, a telescope or even as a dull yellow-orange 'star' with the unaided eye.

Use the Mercury Visibility table to work out when and where to see Mercury next.

Observing Mercury
Choose a location that's high up with a clear horizon to either the west or the east as appropriate for the best views. Places like Dunkery Beacon offer exceptional all-sky views with a flat horizon. Other suitable locations on Exmoor include Porlock Common, Brendon Common, Winsford Hill, Webber's Post (west view only) and Whitstone Post (east view only).

At best you'll be looking for a yellow-orange star against a twilight background no more than 10 – 15 degrees above the horizon. One of the best ways to find Mercury is to use a compass to get a fix on the exact direction over the horizon where it should be and then scan that area with binoculars. ALWAYS MAKE SURE THE SUN IS WELL BELOW THE HORIZON WHEN YOU DO THIS! On the best elongations Mercury sometimes climbs into a darker sky where it becomes more obvious.

So what will you see? With binoculars Mercury appears only as a bright orange-yellow star. A telescope with at least a 130mm aperture will reveal Mercury as a disc of light with changing phases similar to that of our own Moon. In larger telescopes with a mirror size of more than 300mm Mercury's disc displays subtle markings that mottle the planet's surface.

Mercury Transit
On 9 May 2016 and 11 November 2019 Mercury will move across the face of our Sun. Both transit events will be visible from Exmoor – the seven-and-a-half-hour May event being visible in its entirety through the afternoon, and just over four hours of the November event being visible until sundown.

To see the black disc of Mercury move across the Sun you'll need to buy, borrow or hire a small solar telescope, or use a professional full-aperture solar filter in front of a standard astronomical telescope.

Mercury transits across the Sun on 8 November 2006. The tiny planet is the black dot just right of lower centre in the image.
Brocken Inaglory

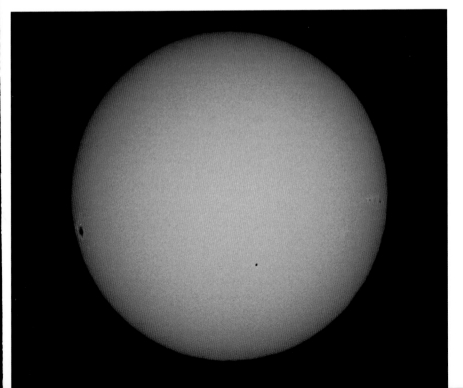

Out beyond the orbit of Mars at a distance of 300 – 500 million kilometres we encounter the asteroid belt – an orbital ring of debris left over from the formation of the solar system some 4.6 billion years ago. The belt consists of more than 200 sun-orbiting asteroids that are larger than 100kms in diameter, along with around 750,000 more chunks of material larger than 1km in size. Distributed among these space rocks there is estimated to be several million asteroid fragments down to the size of a pebble.

What are Asteroids?

Asteroids are composites of rocky material commonly found on and inside all of the inner planets in our solar system, including Earth. Carbonaceous asteroids are the most common and consist of silicate materials and clays. There are also silicaceous asteroids with a higher proportion of silicate materials and nickel iron, and metallic asteroids that are composed mostly of iron. One of the largest asteroids in the belt – the 525-kilometre wide Vesta, which was recently visited by NASA's Dawn Space probe – is one of the more exotic asteroids in the belt. Its surface has been found to be entirely composed of basalt, suggesting perhaps that it was once part of a volcanically active world before it was blasted into space and ended up in the asteroid belt.

Observing Asteroids

As small and as distant as these objects are, amazingly asteroids can be tracked across the sky with binoculars or a small telescope. Larger telescopes reveal more and fainter asteroids, but even telescopes with primary mirrors half a metre wide will not show surface details on asteroids. They are simply too small and too far away.

Identifying an asteroid then from the background stars can be a real challenge. Visually they appear as a point of light with no apparent motion visible with binoculars or at the eyepiece of a telescope. You'll need to use planetarium software like Stellarium (www.stellarium.org) to work out where in the sky you need to be

Top: In 2011 and 2012 NASA's Dawn spacecraft visited Vesta in the asteroid belt. The spacecraft remained in orbit around this tiny world, photo-graphing and mapping it in detail.
NASA /JPL-Caltech/UCAL/MPS/DLR/IDA -

Above: Some asteroids orbit closer to Earth than the main belt. Asteroid 433 Eros is inside the orbit of Mars.
NASA

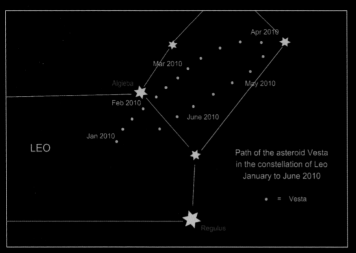

Apr 2010

Mar 2010

Algieba

Feb 2010

May 2010

June 2010

Jan 2010

LEO

Path of the asteroid Vesta
in the constellation of Leo
January to June 2010

● = Vesta

Regulus

Asteroids move
quite slowly against
the background
stars, often
remaining within a
single constellation
for several months
at a time.

Viewing Challenge:
Difficult to see
Equipment: Binoculars /
Telescope
Event Frequency: Very often
Best Views: All year round
Photography Tips:
Asteroids can be captured
photographically using a
tripod-mounted camera and
telephoto lens. A high ISO
setting will be needed along
with an exposure of 20-30
seconds. Alternatively, a
camera or webcam mounted
on a telescope, which is itself
fixed to a motorised equatorial
mount will work. Resulting
images can be stacked
together in image processing
software to bring out more
detail in the star field.

looking for asteroids. Once you've identified the area of sky make a quick sketch of the star field that you see through your binoculars or telescope, or use a tripod-mounted camera equipped with a telephoto lens to image the area of sky. Either will act as your reference point. Revisit the same area of sky a couple of nights later and take the same approach with a sketch or photo image. You'll see that one of the 'stars' will have moved relative to the others in your field of view. If you can work out which one it is that has moved you'll have your asteroid.

10 Brightest Asteroids

#	Asteroid	Distance	Sidereal period	Diameter	Magnitude
No.	Name	10^3 Km	Years	Km	Mag.
1	Ceres	413.5	4.61	932	7.4
2	Pallas	414.2	4.61	524	8.0
3	Juno	398.7	4.36	266	8.7
4	Vesta	352.9	3.63	510	6.5
5	Astraea	385.0	4.14	124	9.8
6	Hebe	362.4	3.78	192	8.3
7	Iris	356.4	3.69	202	7.8
8	Flora	328.9	3.27	140	8.7
9	Metis	356.7	3.69	170	9.1
10	Hygeia	470.8	5.59	428	10.2

Top 10 brightest
asteroids visible
from Exmoor

The Gas Giants – Jupiter and Saturn

Jupiter

AT A DISTANCE of at least 590 million kilometres from Exmoor our journey takes us to the most massive planet in our solar system – Jupiter. Measuring a gigantic 142,800kms across, Jupiter's gargantuan body is 1,300 times the size of Earth. It is composed mostly of a dense molecular hydrogen and helium gas atmosphere several thousand kilometres thick that surrounds a fluid metallic hydrogen layer, which is itself wrapped around a hot dense iron core. In fact conditions at the core are thought to be so extreme that scientists calculate the iron partially melts in the intense heat generated by Jupiter's internal gravitational pressures.

Opposite: Jupiter's inner radiation belts were measured in detail by the Cassini spacecraft in January 2001. Microwave emissions were measured at a frequency of 13.8 gigahertz, indicating the region near Jupiter to be one of the harshest radiation environments in the solar system.
NASA

Left: Jupiter's swirling atmosphere and its Great Red Spot (GRS) are easily seen with a small telescope.
NASA

Jupiter never fails to put on a good show.
Stefano Quaresima

When we look at Jupiter we see the planet's outer atmospheric layers where the temperature is very cold. Here intense 400mph winds draw out the atmosphere into linear bands of alternating dark and light material. The light material is made from highly reflective top-level clouds of frozen ammonia crystals, while the darker bands are slightly warmer lower level layers of atmosphere consisting of methane, ethane, sulphur, phosphorous and water ice.

Observing Jupiter

Jupiter is hard to miss when it's up above the horizon. Other than the Moon and Venus it is the brightest object in the night sky, and is normally visible for nine to ten months every year. Low power binoculars are enough to reveal the planet as a disc, and you might also be able to make out a couple of dark streaks running across the planet's body. If you do you'll have just spotted the two main dark equatorial bands that run all the way around the planet's cold and cloudy atmosphere.

A telescope with a minimum aperture of 150mm will show detail in the two dark bands. Look out for dark barges, spots, bays and other irregularities along their lengths. If you're looking at the right times you might also get to see the Great Red Spot, a 300-year old storm feature that is twice the size of the Earth. Often it appears as a dark grey eye, notched into the southern edge of the southern equatorial belt.

Best times to see Jupiter from Exmoor.

Jupiter From Exmoor

VISIBLE MORNING SKY	VISIBLE EVENING SKY	OPPOSITION DATE	BEST VIEWS
Sep 2014 - Apr 2015	Dec 2014 - Jun 2015	February 6th 2015 (Cancer Constellation)	Oct 2014-May 2015
Oct 2015 - May 2016	Jan 2016 - Aug 2016	March 8th 2016 (Leo Constellation)	Nov 2015-Jun 2016
Nov 2016 - Jun 2017	Feb 2017 - Aug 2017	April 7th 2017 (Virgo Constellation)	Dec 2016-Jun 2017
Dec 2017 - Jun 2018	Apr 2018 - Oct 2018	May 9th 2018 (Libra Constellation)	Jan 2018-Jul 2018
Jan 2019 - Jul 2019	May 2019 - Nov 2019	June 10th 2019 (Ophiuchus Constellation)	Feb 2019-Aug 2019

Jupiter's
atmosphere is
constantly
changing. These
are the belts and
zones that are
normally visible.
Sometimes they
merge and /or
disappear.
NASA

Below left:
Jupiter's Southern
Equatorial Belt
disappeared
from view for
several months
during 2010.
Sketch by Seb Jay

Below right: Transit
of Ganymede and
Ganymede's
shadow across
Jupiter on 28
November 2012.
Sketch by Seb Jay

Jupiter's observable atmosphere is pretty dynamic. The planet rotates on its axis at immense speed, making one full rotation in around 9 hours and 50 minutes. You only have to watch Jupiter for 20 – 30 minutes to see appreciable movement of the planet's atmospheric features over the disc as they churn their way around the planet.

On occasion there are more dramatic changes to witness. In 2010 the dark southern equatorial belt faded and disappeared altogether for seven months. It then re-appeared in spectacular fashion in early 2011, after which it showed spectacular white rifts through the belt. Events like these often happen without warning making Jupiter such a fascinating planet to watch.

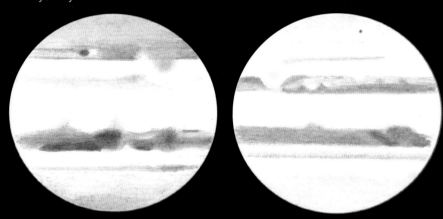

Jupiter's Moons

When looking at Jupiter through binoculars or a telescope you won't fail to notice 1 – 4 bright points of light flanking the planet in line with the direction of the planet's dark belts. These are Jupiter's brightest moons: Io, Ganymede, Europa and Callisto. The time taken for each moon to orbit Jupiter is different. Io is the quickest, completing an orbit in just 1.77 days. Callisto is the longest and completes her orbit every 16.7 days.

As seen from Earth the moons sometimes pass directly in front of Jupiter. When they do distant sunlight illuminates their passage, throwing down a small dark shadow onto the gas giant's visible surface. These 'shadow transits' can be seen in telescopes of 150mm aperture and larger, the moon's shadow itself revealed as a small dark spot on Jupiter's disc. If you watch closely you'll see the shadow move stealthily over the planet's surface. Look closer still and you might be able to make out a small brighter dot of light following the same trajectory, but some way behind or in front of the shadow. If you do then you might well have spotted the moon itself in transit across Jupiter!

Saturn

If there's one planet in our solar system capable of delivering that instant wow-factor it's Saturn. Even though it is never closer to us than 1.2 billion kilometres, any telescope with an aperture of 75mm and above yields a crisp view of the planet and its rings. Larger telescopes bring bigger and brighter views; telescopes with

View from Saturn (Cassini)
900 million miles away

Viewing Challenge:
Easy to see
Equipment: Eyes /
Binoculars / Telescope
Event Frequency: Often
Best Views: Jupiter is visible from Exmoor for around nine months of every year.
Photography Tips: Jupiter is bright enough to photograph by just holding a camera to the telescope's eyepiece. Use a high ISO and exposures of 1/250 to 1/100 seconds. High resolution images can be captured using a camera or webcam mounted directly to a telescope, which is itself mounted on a motorised equatorial platform. For best results shoot several images and stack them together in image processing software.

On 19 July 2013 the Cassini Spacecraft in orbit around Saturn turned its camera to Earth and photographed us. Everyone you know lives on that pale blue dot.
NASA/JPL-Caltech/ Space Science Institute

apertures above 200mm offering glimpses of Saturn's more elusive features, such as the Cassini Division – a 3500km wide gap in the rings encircling the planet – and even storm systems in the planet's upper atmosphere.

To be seen as clearly as this over such a distance it should come as no surprise to learn that Saturn is a real giant of a planet. It is only slightly smaller than Jupiter in real terms, its equatorial diameter measuring some 120,000kms – large enough to contain 760 Earths. Like Jupiter its huge gaseous atmosphere is composed mostly of molecular hydrogen and helium gas. Its dense atmosphere sinks to a viscous then liquid layer of hydrogen and helium, which itself surrounds a small dense and very hot iron core.

Saturn is known to be the windiest place in the solar system. Jet stream movement in Saturn's atmosphere has been recorded at up to 1800km/hr. Like Jupiter Saturn also emits heat from its interior. In Saturn's case it is a lot of heat – as much as twice the energy it receives from the Sun. Latest research indicates its heat output is not constant. The reasons why this should be are not yet known.

Best times to see Saturn from Exmoor.

Saturn From Exmoor

VISIBLE MORNING SKY	VISIBLE EVENING SKY	OPPOSITION DATE	BEST VIEWS
Jan 2015 - Jun 2015	Apr 2015 - Sep 2015	May 23rd 2015 (Libra Constellation)	Feb 2015-Aug 2015
Jan 2016 - Jul 2016	May 2016 - Oct 2016	June 3rd 2016 (Ophiuchus Constellation)	Feb 2016-Sep 2016
Feb 2017 - Jul 2017	May 2017 - Nov 2017	June 15th 2017 (Ophiuchus Constellation)	Mar 2017-Oct 2017
Feb 2018 - Aug 2018	May 2018 - Nov 2018	June 27th 2018 (Sagittarius Constellation)	Mar 2018-Oct 2018
Mar 2019 - Aug 2019	Jun 2019 - Dec 2019	July 9th 2019 (Sagittarius Constellation)	Apr 2019-Nov 2019

The 2011 Saturnian storm caught as a sketch. Seb Jay

Observing Saturn

Saturn can easily be seen with the naked eye. It appears as a fairly bright golden yellow-orange coloured 'star', but never rivals the brilliance of Venus or Jupiter in the night sky, and is often dimmer than Mars.

The ringed planet completes a full orbit of the Sun every twenty-nine-and-a-half-years. During this time Saturn rotates about its tilted axis of 26.7°, and moves relative to the Earth in its orbit by an angle of up to 2.5°. These factors combined cause the angle of Saturn and its rings to change from our viewpoint here on Exmoor.

Every fourteen – sixteen years we see Saturn with its rings edge on to us. The last time this happened was in 2009. Since then the rings have gradually opened up year-on-year as the northern hemisphere tilts further towards us. By June 2017 Saturn's

Saturn photographed next to the Moon using a Canon IXUS compact and a small refractor in May 2007. Cedric Allier

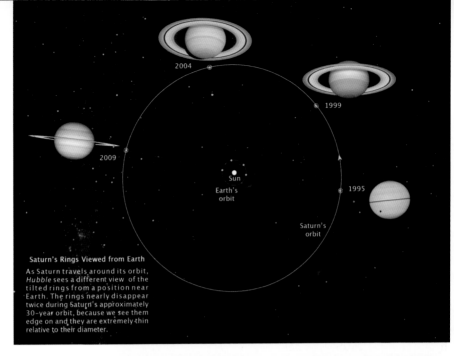

2004

1999

2009

Sun

Earth's
orbit

1995

Saturn's
orbit

Saturn's Rings Viewed from Earth
As Saturn travels around its orbit,
Hubble sees a different view of the
tilted rings from a position near
Earth. The rings nearly disappear
twice during Saturn's approximately
30-year orbit, because we see them
edge on and they are extremely thin
relative to their diameter.

Above: The angle of
Saturn's rings as
seen from Earth
changes through
the course of the
planet's near
thirty-year orbit
around the Sun.
Image Credit NASA,
ESA, and the Hubble
Heritage Team
(STScI/AURA)

Right: Saturnian
moon transits as
imaged by the
Hubble Space
Telescope. Titan is
the large dusky
orange disc at
upper right.
Enceladus and Dione
are to the left.
Image Credit NASA,
ESA, and the Hubble
Heritage Team
(STScI/AURA)

northern hemisphere will be maximally tilted towards Earth giving
us the widest open view of the rings for some time, and making
more elusive ring features like ring spokes easier to see.

As with Jupiter Saturn is a fast spinner. It completes a full night-
day rotation in just over 10 hours, the immense spin forces
involved flattening the poles and bloating the planet's equatorial
region. You can see this squashed globe affect quite clearly with a
telescope. On the globe itself Saturn's features are similar to those
of Jupiter but a lot more muted. You might be able to make out
one or two of the planet's equatorial belts as dull brown stripes

across the pale yellow disc. Occasionally low-contrast spots and storm features also emerge, as happened in the spring of 2011 when a giant thunderstorm system burst through the top of Saturn's upper cloud decks in its northern hemisphere. Ten thousand times more powerful than our thunderstorms here on Earth this gigantic convective storm was bigger than the entire Earth itself. It raged for months, churning up the upper atmosphere as it moved across the disc, leaving in its wake a bright band behind the head of the storm. The views were spectacular in telescopes of 200mm aperture and larger.

Saturn appears clearly and in high definition through large amateur telescopes.
Avani Soares

Saturn's Moons

Sixty-two moons are in orbit around Saturn. On a moonless night from Exmoor it is possible to see the six brightest ones using a 150mm or 200mm aperture telescope. Most obvious of all, and visible with binoculars, is mysterious Titan. Shrouded in a visually opaque dense nitrogen and methane atmosphere this orange speck of light is home to a liquid world. Beneath its cloak exists hydrocarbon lakes and river deltas, which were glimpsed spectacularly by the descending Huygens space probe lander in early 2005.

Rhea, Tethys and Dione are the next most visible of Saturn's moons. They are a good deal fainter than Titan and so are more difficult to see. You'll find them closer in to Saturn than Titan as all three have tighter orbital paths around the planet from our viewing point.

Iapetus and tiny Enceladus take us to the limit of what we can reasonably see of Saturn's moons from Exmoor with a portable telescope. Iapetus is slightly less dim than Enceladus but more difficult to spot as it takes a highly inclined orbital route around Saturn compared to the other visible moons.

At just 505kms wide it is a miracle that we can see Enceladus at all from Exmoor. The reason we can see it is that it is coated almost entirely in water ice, and so is one of the most reflective objects in the solar system. It may also harbour a secret beneath its -200°c surface. The Cassini space probe, currently in orbit around Saturn, has detected giant plumes of water and organic materials blasting off the surface of this tiny moon. The mechanism driving these powerful jets is unknown.

Viewing Challenge:
Easy to see
Equipment: Eyes / Binoculars / Telescope
Event Frequency: Saturn is visible from Exmoor for around nine months of every year.
Photography Tips: Saturn is bright enough to photograph by just holding a camera to the telescope's eyepiece. Use a high ISO and exposures of 1/250 to 1/100 seconds. High resolution images can be captured using a camera or webcam mounted directly to a telescope, which is itself mounted on a motorised equatorial platform. For best results shoot several images and stack them together in image processing software.

Neptune was visited
by the Voyager 2
spacecraft in 1989.
NASA

The Outer Gas Planets – Uranus & Neptune

Uranus

RESIDING IN AN eighty-four-year orbit around the Sun more than 2.6 billion kilometres from Earth is the outer gas planet Uranus. Discovered by William Herschel in 1781 Uranus is so remote that it takes sunlight (travelling at 299,792,458 metres per second) two hours and forty minutes to reach it. Amazingly, even at this distance, Uranus can be seen from Exmoor with the naked eye. It's not easy to identify as it looks just like a dim star on the edge of the visible sky. But, with a decent star chart to hand, it can be done!

Uranus is a ringed planet. The rings are so tenuous and faint that they cannot be seen with a portable telescope from Exmoor. Instead it takes a telescope like Hubble to photograph them directly.
NASA / ESA

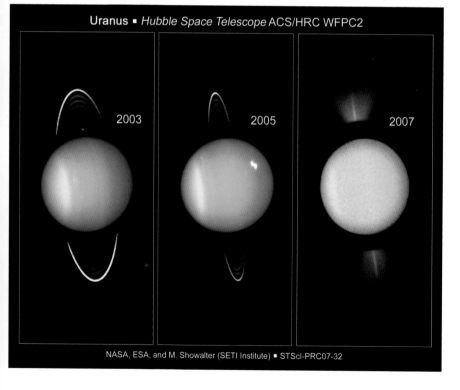

Uranus ▪ *Hubble Space Telescope* ACS/HRC WFPC2

2003   2005   2007

NASA, ESA, and M. Showalter (SETI Institute) ▪ STScl-PRC07-32

Uranus From Exmoor

VISIBLE MORNING SKY	VISIBLE EVENING SKY	OPPOSITION DATE	BEST VIEWS
Jul 2014 - Dec 2014	Aug 2014 - Feb 2015	October 7th 2014 (Pisces Constellation)	Aug 2014-Jan 2015
Jul 2015 - Dec 2015	Aug 2015 - Mar 2016	October 12th 2015 (Pisces Constellation)	Aug 2015-Feb 2016
Jul 2016 - Dec 2016	Aug 2016 - Mar 2017	October 15th 2016 (Pisces Constellation)	Aug 2016-Feb 2017
Jul 2017 - Dec 2017	Aug 2017 - Mar 2018	October 19th 2017 (Pisces Constellation)	Aug 2017-Feb 2018
Jul 2018 - Dec 2018	Aug 2018 - Mar 2019	October 24th 2018 (Aries Constellation)	Aug 2018-Feb 2019
Jul 2019 - Jan 2020	Aug 2019 - Mar 2020	October 28th 2019 (Aries Constellation)	Sep 2019-Feb 2020

Viewing Challenge: Moderately challenging
Equipment: Binoculars / Telescope
Event Frequency: Often
Best Views: Uranus is visible from Exmoor for eight months of the year.
Photography Tips: If you know where to look then Uranus is best captured using a camera or webcam mounted directly to a telescope, which is itself mounted on an equatorial platform. Alternatively, a camera with a large telephoto lens can be used to shoot images of the area over several nights to see the planet's movement against the background stars. moderate to high ISO.

Through binoculars or a telescope Uranus is easier to identify. A telescope of 200mm aperture at x200 magnification or more will resolve the planet into a tiny blue-green disc. Its colour is down to the outer layer of methane clouds wrapped around the planet, which reflect sunlight in blue and green wavelengths. Below this outer methane envelope we find an icy cold atmosphere of gaseous hydrogen, helium and even more methane. Uranus in fact has the coldest recorded atmosphere in the solar system at a temperature of minus -224°c. Deep down the planet's core is most likely composed of rock and ice with very little if any heat generation.

Amateur astronomers who study Uranus in large telescopes have at times seen subtle atmospheric details on the planet's tiny disc. Faint latitudinal bands have been seen as well as subtle shading on other areas of the disc. You need to be dedicated to find these details as they are not at all easy to see.

Even at 2.6 billion kilometres away a keen eye can still see detail in the planet's methane atmosphere.
Sketch by Dr Paul Abel .

54

Uranus Observation

2013 October 06, Start: 2218UT Finish: 2255UT

203mm Newtonian Reflector, x250 & x312
Integrated light only.

Seeing:All-III, Transparency: Excellent,
B= 22.5, Ds= 22.6, Disk Diameter= 3.7"

proc.

north

Drawing: 2225UT, x312, CM: 47, Seeing:All-III   Paul G. Abel, Leicester UK.

Neptune appears only as a tiny blue disc, even in large telescopes. Stefano Quaresima.

Neptune

Since the demotion of Pluto to *dwarf planet* status in 2006 Neptune is now recognised as the furthest classical planet from the Sun in our solar system. It never gets any closer to Earth than 4.3 billion kilometres in its 164-year long orbit, and remains below naked eye visibility even on the darkest of Exmoor nights.

Neptune is 57 times larger than Earth. The immense distance between the two planets though means that to resolve Neptune into a disc you will need at least a 200mm aperture telescope at x200 magnification. As with Uranus, the top visible layers of Neptune's atmosphere consist of methane clouds. They reflect light at blue wavelengths giving the planet a deep blue-grey hue, which can easily be seen with a telescope.

Beneath the methane cloud deck ferocious winds in excess of 1,000km/hr whip through dense and cold gaseous layers of molecular hydrogen, helium and further methane. Ammonia ice, methane ice and water ice have also been detected in trace amounts in Neptune's minus -220°c atmosphere. Colder still is Neptune's largest Moon, Triton.

Viewing Challenge: Moderately challenging
Equipment: Binoculars / Telescope
Event Frequency: Often
Best Views: Neptune is visible from Exmoor for eight months of the year.
Photography Tips: If you know where to look then Neptune is best captured using a camera or webcam mounted directly to a telescope, which is itself mounted on an equatorial platform. Alternatively, a camera with a large telephoto lens can be used to shoot images of the area over several nights to see the planet's movement against the background stars.

Neptune From Exmoor

VISIBLE MORNING SKY	VISIBLE EVENING SKY	OPPOSITION DATE	BEST VIEWS
Jun 2014 - Oct 2014	Aug 2014 - Jan 2015	August 29th 2014 (Aquarius Constellation)	Aug 2014-Dec 2014
Jun 2015 - Oct 2015	Aug 2015 - Jan 2016	September 1st 2015 (Aquarius Constellation)	Aug 2015-Dec 2015
Jun 2016 - Oct 2016	Aug 2016 - Jan 2017	September 2nd 2016 (Aquarius Constellation)	Aug 2016-Dec 2016
Jun 2017 - Oct 2017	Aug 2017 - Jan 2018	September 5th 2017 (Aquarius Constellation)	Aug 2017-Dec 2017
Jun 2018 - Oct 2018	Aug 2018 - Jan 2019	September 7th 2018 (Aquarius Constellation)	Aug 2018-Dec 2018
Jun 2019 - Oct 2019	Aug 2019 - Feb 2020	September 10th 2019 (Aquarius Constellation)	Aug 2019-Jan 2020

Only slightly smaller than our own Moon, Triton's solid icy surface has been recorded at minus -232°c, making it one of the coldest places in the solar system. A moonless night and a telescope of at least 250mm aperture are needed to see this tiny frozen world. It's not a sight that will take your breath away for sure as Triton appears like a very faint pale star. But just the fact that you're seeing something smaller than our Moon 4.3 billion kilometres away can be quite a special moment!

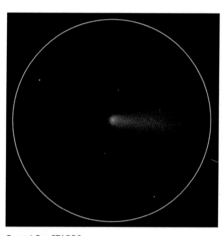

Comet PanSTARRS was prominent in small telescopes from March to May 2013.
Sketch by Seb Jay.

Comets

Way out beyond Neptune we find a graveyard of icy celestial bodies. Millions, if not trillions, of relics from the formation of the solar system drift around the Sun in long-term orbits, some taking millennia to complete a solar circuit in a region of space known as the Oort Cloud. Every now and then gravitational interactions in the Cloud send one of these icy chunks rushing in towards the inner solar system, caught by the immense gravitational pull of our Sun. As they fall inwards they begin to defrost in the Sun's glare, forming a plume of ionised gas and rock dust debris behind them. We see this process in action from Earth as a comet with a tail.

Observing Comets

Exmoor's dark skies make it easy to see comets in all their glory. In 1996 Comet Hyakutake appeared high in the sky over Exmoor with a dust tail that spread 40° across the heavens. It was an easy naked eye object, and looked spectacular only because Exmoor's dark sky background helped bring out the comet's reflected light. A year later Comet Hale-Bopp lit up the morning and evening skies in similar fashion.

If you got to see both of them you were lucky. Naked eye comets aren't all that common, occurring on average once every five – ten years. Much more frequent are the fainter comets that can be seen only with binoculars or a telescope. On average there are at least 1 – 2 comets every year that can be spotted with a 150mm

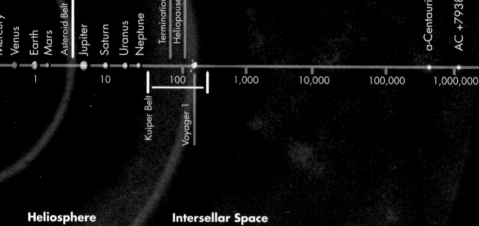

Mercury
Venus
Earth
Mars
Asteroid Belt
Jupiter
Saturn
Uranus
Neptune
Termination Shock
Heliopause
Oort Cloud
α-Centauri
AC +793888

1   10   100   1,000   10,000   100,000   1,000,000

Kuiper Belt
Voyager 1

Heliosphere   **Intersellar Space**

A simple way to understand distances across the solar system and in near interstellar space is to use the distance between the Earth and the Sun as a unit of measurement. In kilometres this distance is just slightly less than 150 million km. We can call this distance 1 Astronomical Unit or 1AU. Using this measurement the distance between the Sun and Saturn is 10AU, and to the edge of interstellar space is over 100AU. Hannah Collier

Comet Garradd sported two tails that pointed in opposite directions during its passage through our skies in 2012.
Dave Eagle

aperture telescope. A 300mm aperture telescopes gains you access to about 3 – 4 comets each year. Many of them reveal themselves to be that classic comet shape, but in miniature.

Viewing Challenge:
Easy to see
Equipment: Eyes /
Binoculars / Telescope
Event Frequency: Occasional
Best Views: Evening and
morning skies when a comet
is close to the Sun. This is
when a comet is at its brightest.
Some comets track higher in
the sky after their journey
around the Sun. They are
fainter than when at close
approach but higher up and
so are easier to see.
Photography Tips: Brighter
comets can easily be captured
with a camera on a tripod
using 10 – 20 second
exposures on a high ISO
setting. Fainter comets are
best captured using a camera
or webcam mounted directly
to a telescope, which is itself
mounted on a motorised
equatorial platform. For best
results shoot several images
and stack them together in
image processing software.

Comet
Hale-Bopp lit
up the skies in
1997. It is widely
regarded as the
most spectacular
naked eye comet
in recent times.
Dave Eagle

Occasionally some comets surprise us by showing more than one
tail. Comet Garradd in 2012 gave us two tails pointing in opposite
directions!

The Milky Way

LOOK UP FROM Exmoor on a moonless night during the summer, autumn or winter months and you won't fail to notice a band of faint starlight stretching its way across the darkness from horizon to horizon. What you're seeing is the Milky Way – the starlight from more than 300 billion suns that make up our home galaxy.

Opposite: The winter Milky Way takes in Orion the Hunter and the famous red giant Betelgeuse.
Luca Argalia

Our naked eye view gives us the big picture. Summer and early autumn evenings sees the Cygnus arm of the Milky Way overhead with its giant dark rift running through the Summer Triangle. Down close to the southern horizon we see the Scutum Star Cloud, a patch of bright fuzzy starlight that for all the world can look like a regular Earth cloud coming to spoil the view! It's that bright and obvious.

The Sagittarius arm of the Milky Way is also on view, bobbing along the horizon. Looking in this direction we are staring right into the centre of our galaxy where a supermassive black hole lurks, 4 million times the mass of our own Sun.

Winter months see the Perseus arm of the Milky Way above us. We also see the local Orion arm drifting down through the constellation of Orion the Hunter. It sweeps past the red supergiant, Betelgeuse, taking in Sirius the brightest star visible in the night sky from Exmoor, en-route to the horizon.

The summer Milky Way crosses through the Summer Triangle and reaches down through Scutum and Sagittarius.
Mike Meal

The Milky Way

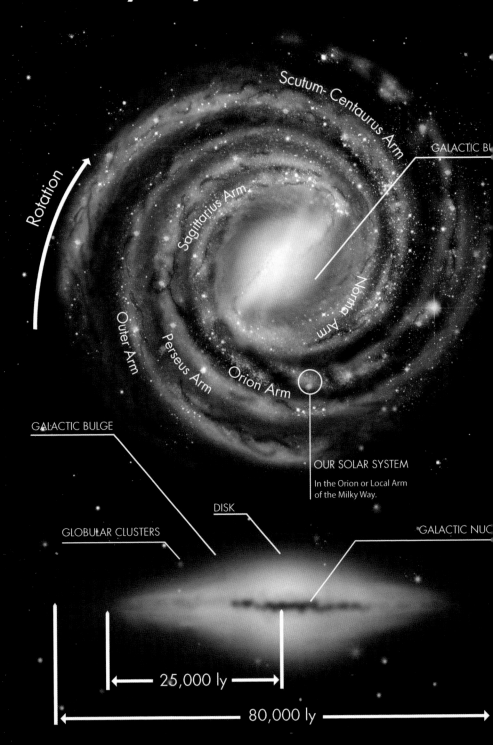

Rotation

Scutum- Centaurus Arm

GALACTIC B[

Sagittarius Arm

Norma Arm

Outer Arm

Perseus Arm

Orion Arm

GALACTIC BULGE

OUR SOLAR SYSTEM

In the Orion or Local Arm
of the Milky Way.

GLOBULAR CLUSTERS

DISK

GALACTIC NUC

25,000 ly

80,000 ly

Size and Distance

In the context of the Universe, the Milky Way is a small spiral galaxy amid billions. It is not especially large, and it isn't the smallest. However, compared to the size and distance of the solar system our home galaxy is immense, so immense in fact that we have to switch to a different unit of measurement to understand just how big it is. This unit is the light year, which is the distance covered by light in one year when travelling at 299,792,458 metres per second. Put into the context of kilometres that is a distance of nearly nine and a half trillion kilometres per year. Latest research tells us that the Milky Way is 100,000 light years in diameter. Travelling at the speed of light it would therefore take us 100,000 years to cross it – a distance equivalent to ninety-five thousand trillion kilometres.

Opposite: The Milky Way is a spiral galaxy. The bulk of our galaxy's stars are arranged in spiral arms rotating around a massive central black hole. In the darker areas between the arms we still find stars, they are just not as densely packed as we find in the spiral arms.
Hannah Collier.

Observing the Milky Way

Embedded within the spiral arms of the Milky Way are stars at all stages of stellar life. Binoculars and telescopes reveal double and multiple star systems mingling with gigantic stellar nurseries where new stars are being born. There are stars like our Sun out there, and stars much bigger, brighter and younger than our Sun burning up their reserves of hydrogen and helium at a furious rate.

We also find stars older and colder than our Sun, and stars on the cusp of stellar death. On occasion we can even see stars crossover into the 'afterlife' when they explode as supernovae. It's a rare event, but it does happen – and has happened in the past. Right across the galaxy we see the remnants of long-past explosions; dense compact cores of dead stars now exposed to view, while the rest of its materials lie scattered around it as a nebula. It's all there for us to see.

Viewing Challenge: Easy to see
Equipment: Eyes / Binoculars / Telescope
Event Frequency: Occasional
Best Views: Summer, autumn and winter when the Milky Way is overhead.
Photography Tips: From Exmoor a twenty to thirty-second exposure using a modern DSLR or mirrorless Compact System Camera at a high ISO setting will be enough to capture the glory of the Milky Way on a moonless night. Use a fast wide angle lens for best results and use a wide aperture.

The Pole Star & Circumpolar Constellations

If there is one star in the night sky that is familiar by name it is Polaris – the Pole Star or North Star. I say familiar by name as plenty of people have heard about the Pole Star; fewer people can actually identify it in the night sky.

From Exmoor the Pole Star is not the brightest star in the sky, nor is the highest star in the sky. In fact, compared to some of the more obvious star patterns that make up the constellations across the heavens, the Pole Star is rather inconspicuous.

So why does the Pole Star have such familiarity? As far back as Ancient Greece the Pole Star has been recognised as an important navigational aid. Its point in the sky hovers over the direction of True North and never changes. It is the only star in the northern

Looking north on Exmoor.
Adrian Cubitt - ATV Productions Ltd

Star trails over the National Park Centre at Dunster. Adrian Cubitt - ATV Productions Ltd

hemisphere sky that appears to remain at a fixed point – a constant reminder of where north is throughout the night and throughout the year.

The reason for its unique behaviour has nothing to do with the star itself. Instead it's our observing location that makes it special. Earth's axis is tilted to its orbital plane by 23.5°. Project a line centrally through this axis into the night sky and we find that it passes to within a fraction of a degree of Polaris. The Pole Star therefore marks out the location of Earth's axis of rotation on the celestial sphere – a position in the sky known as the north celestial pole. It is the pivot point around which all other stars appear to move as Earth spins through its twenty-four hours, and around which the stars appear to pivot through the seasons as Earth shuffles along its orbit around the Sun.

This process is no more sweetly visualised than in star trail photography. If you've ever seen a star trails image where the trails curve around a static point in the sky, you're seeing the effect of Earth's rotation while looking along the axis of that rotation towards the north celestial pole.

The path of the north celestial pole traced out as a 23.5° circle among the stars. Negative numbers are years BC. Positive numbers are years AD. Tau'olunga.

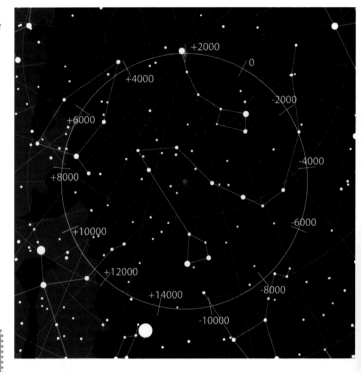

Precession

You might think that it is rather fortuitous that the north celestial pole is marked out by a relatively bright star. It hasn't always been this way, and won't always be so in the future. The pull of the Sun and the Moon's gravity on Earth causes a phenomenon known as precession. It shifts the position of the north celestial pole relative to the background stars, tracing out a circle in the heavens over a 23.5° radius in a cycle lasting 25,800 years. Five thousand years ago this meant that the projection of Earth's axis was close to Alpha Draconis (Thuban). In eight thousand years time Alpha Cygni (Deneb) will be the closest bright star to the north celestial pole.

How to Find the Pole Star

The Pole Star is actually very easy to find. Use a compass to work out the direction of magnetic north, then, facing north, look up in the sky at an angle to the horizon that is equivalent to your latitude. For Exmoor this is approximately 51°degrees above the horizon. The star that you'll find there is the Pole Star.

Another way to track it down is to use the two circumpolar constellations of Ursa Major (The Plough / Great Bear) and Cassiopeia, the latter of which appears as a giant 'W' star pattern in the sky. Both constellations remain above the horizon all year round, tracing out a circle in north-facing skies as they complete their annual journeys around the Pole Star as we see it from our observing location.

Fortuitously, Ursa Major and Cassiopeia are roughly the same distance away from Polaris, but on opposite sides. All you have to do is find the constellations with the help of the star maps in this book and look at the equidistance point between them. The main star that you see there will be the Pole Star.

The Pole Star is easy to find from Exmoor. Just look north 51-degrees above the horizon. The brightest star you find in that location is the Pole Star.

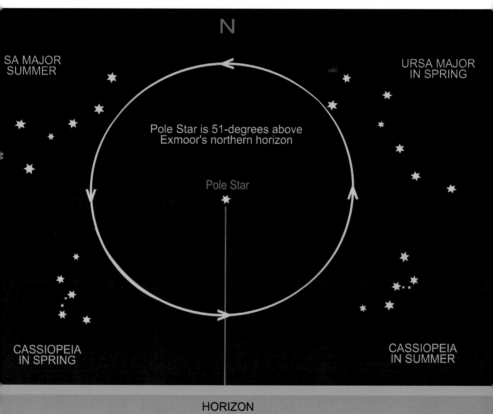

N

SA MAJOR
SUMMER

URSA MAJOR
IN SPRING

Pole Star is 51-degrees above
Exmoor's northern horizon

Pole Star

CASSIOPEIA
IN SPRING

CASSIOPEIA
IN SUMMER

HORIZON

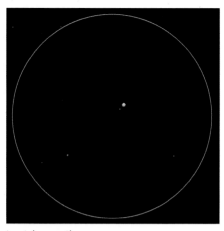

In a telescope the Pole Star is split into a bright primary star and a dim secondary star. Sketch by Seb Jay

Opposite: The main stages of stellar evolution are captured on a Hertzsprung-Russell (HR) Diagram. Most stars spend their time on the main sequence before evolving into Giants. At the end of the Giant stage they cast off their remaining gases leaving behind a dense white dwarf star, which slowly cools and dims. Large stars evolve differently as Supergiants. At the end of their lives they might leave behind a neutron star or a black hole instead of a white dwarf.

Observing the Pole Star

Polaris is 434 light years away from Exmoor. It shines with a light that left its surface in the 1580s during the reign of Elizabeth I – more than a quarter of a century before the invention of the telescope. Put another way you're seeing starlight from the 1580s. How's that for time travel!

From Exmoor any telescope with an aperture larger than 60mm will show Polaris to not be just one star but two: a bright pale yellow-white primary and a fainter dull white secondary star. In reality the brighter star is a supergiant 50 times larger than our Sun, while the secondary star is a smaller main sequence companion separated from it by more than 300 billion kilometres – or 12 light days. The two stars orbit around a common centre of gravity over many thousands of years. Because of this gravitational link Polaris is classified as a true binary star. More details on star classifications are given in the next section.

The Brightest Stars

The brightest stars in Exmoor's night sky all reside inside our own galaxy. They vary in distance from 8 light years to 1,500 light years away. It is worth noting that the brightest stars are not necessarily the closest ones to us, as not all stars are the same size, or have the same luminosity.

Hot Blue-White Stars

The bluer a star appears to our eyes the hotter and more luminous it is physically. The beautiful star Vega in the constellation of Lyra is the third brightest star in Exmoor's night sky. Train a telescope on this sparkling gem – you can't miss it in the summer and autumn as it forms the upper right star in the Summer Triangle – and you'll see it shines a steely blue-white colour.

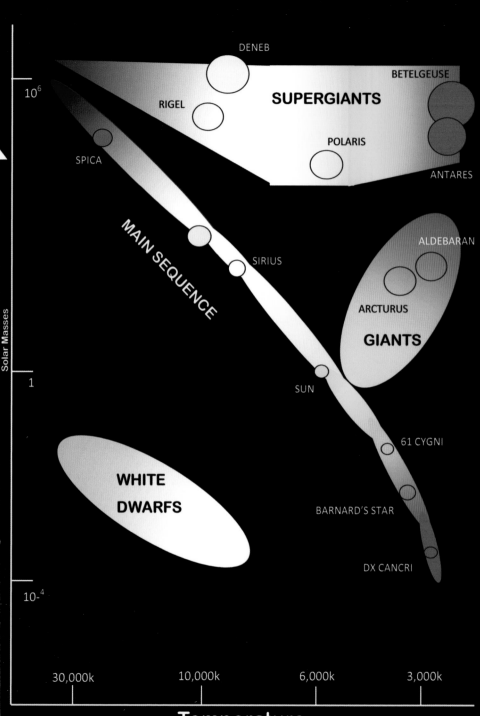

Vega is 25 light years away from us. It is 3 times larger than our Sun and some 58 times more luminous with a surface temperature of around 9,500 degrees Celsius. If we were at Vega looking back at our Sun, our home star would appear as an insignificant yellow point of light visible to the naked eye but not outstanding, melting into the Milky Way background.

Across the sky to the left of Vega at the upper-left point of the Summer Triangle is the white star Deneb. To us here on Exmoor Deneb is only marginally fainter than Vega. But in the reality of space-time it is at least 60 times further away from us than Vega with an estimated distance from Earth of at least 1,500 light years. That makes Deneb one of the most distant stars that we can see from Exmoor with the naked eye. On a hypothetical planet orbiting Deneb our Sun would only just be visible in a large telescope as a faint dot of yellow light.

This all throws out an intriguing conclusion: for Deneb to be nearly as bright as Vega, but so much further away, Deneb must really be huge. Studies show this to be the case. Deneb is now known to be a blue-white supergiant 200 times larger than our own Sun, twice as hot, and some 250,000 times more luminous.

For the hottest and bluest star visible to the naked eye from Exmoor we have to travel into the spring sky and seek out Spica. At approximately 22,500°c Spica is nearly four times hotter than our Sun. We see it as the eleventh brightest star in the sky from inside the International Dark Sky Reserve, putting on a magnificent performance in a telescope where its blue colour really shows. At 220 light years away Spica is nearly 9 times more distant from our shores than Vega, and more than 200 times more luminous.

Cool Orange-Red Stars

Not all of the brightest stars under Exmoor's dark skies are hot and blue. At the other end of the spectrum we have bright orange and orange-red stars. These stars are significantly cooler with surface temperatures of around 3,000 – 4,000 degrees Celsius. Perhaps the most famous orange-red star is Betelgeuse in the constellation of Orion.

15 Brightest Stars in Exmoor's Night Sky

STAR	STAR MAGNITUDE	CONSTELLATION	DISTANCE	VISIBLE
Sirius	-1.46	Canis Major	8.6 light years	Winter
Arcturus	-0.04	Bootes	34 light years	Spring
Vega	+0.03	Lyra	25 light years	Summer
Capella	+0.08	Auriga	41 light years	Winter
Rigel	+0.12	Orion	850 light years	Winter
Procyon	+0.38	Canis Minor	11.4 light years	Winter
Betelgeuse	+0.50	Orion	600 light years	Winter
Altair	+0.77	Aquila	16 light years	Summer
Aldebaran	+0.85	Taurus	65 light years	Autumn
Antares	+0.96	Scorpio	550 light years	Summer
Spica	+0.98	Virgo	220 light years	Spring
Pollux	+1.14	Gemini	40 light years	Winter
Fomalhaut	+1.16	Piscis Austrinus	22 light years	Autumn
Deneb	+1.25	Cygnus	1500 light years	Summer
Regulus	+1.35	Leo	77 light years	Spring

15 Closest Stars in Exmoor's Night Sky

STAR	STAR MAGNITUDE	CONSTELLATION	DISTANCE	VISIBLE
Barnard's Star	+9.53	Ophiuchus	5.96 light years	Summer
Wolf 359	+13.44	Leo	7.78 light years	Spring
Lalande 21185	+7.47	Ursa Major	8.29 light years	Spring
Sirius	-1.46	Canis Major	8.6 light years	Winter
Luyten 726-8	+12.54	Cetus	8.72 light years	Autumn
V1216 Sagittarii	+10.43	Sagittarius	9.68 light years	Summer
HH Andromedae	+12.29	Andromeda	10.32 light years	Autumn
Epsilon Eridani	+3.73	Eridanus	10.52 light years	Winter
FI Virginis	+11.13	Virgo	10.92 light years	Spring
EZ Aquarii	+13.27	Aquarius	11.26 light years	Autumn
Procyon	+0.38	Canis Minor	11.4 light years	Winter
61 Cygni	+5.21	Cygnus	11.4 light years	Summer
Struve 2398	+8.90	Draco	11.52 light years	All Year
GX Andromedae	+8.08	Andromeda	11.62 light years	Autumn
Tau Ceti	+3.49	Cetus	11.88 light years	Autumn

15 Brightest Stars Visible from Exmoor with Confirmed Exoplanets

STAR	STAR MAGNITUDE	CONSTELLATION	DISTANCE	CONFIRMED PLANETS	VISIBLE
Pollux	+1.15	Gemini	34 light years	1	Winter
Fomalhaut	+1.16	Piscis Austrinus	22 light years	1	Autumn
Alpha Arietis	+2.00	Aries	66 light years	1	Autumn
Gamma Leonis	+2.12	Leo	130 light years	1	Spring
Gamma Cephei	+3.23	Cepheus	46 light years	1	All Year
Iota Draconis	+3.31	Draco	101 light years	1	All Year
Epsilon Tauri	+3.54	Taurus	147 light years	1	Winter
Epsilon Eridani	+3.73	Eridanus	10.5 light years	1	Winter
7 CanisMajoris	+3.97	Canis Major	64 light years	1	Winter
Upsilon Andromedae	+4.09	Andromeda	44 light years	4	Autumn
91 Aquarii	+4.21	Aquarius	150 light years	1	Autumn
HD 60532	+4.46	Puppis	83 light years	2	Winter
Tau Bootis	+4.50	Bootes	51 light years	1	Spring
Chi Virginis	+4.66	Virgo	294 light years	1	Spring
Xi Aquilae	+4.72	Aquila	184 light years	1	Summer

Above: The brightest 15 stars visible from Exmoor that have confirmed planets orbiting them.

Right: Scale of magnitudes used for measuring apparent brightness of objects in the sky

Star Magnitudes Scale

BRIGHTEST

-26	The Sun
-13	Full Moon
-6	Crescent Moon
-4	Venus at its brightest
-2	Jupiter at its brightest
-1.5	Brightest star (Sirius)
0	Vega
+1	Saturn at its brightest
+2	Pole Star (Polaris)
+6.8	Limit of star visibility to the naked eye from Exmoor
+10.5	Limit of star visibility in 10x50 binoculars
+13.5	Limit of star visibility in a 150mm aperture telescope
+15.0	Limit of star visibility in a 300mm aperture telescope

FAINTEST

Betelgeuse is one of the most massive stars known. It is approximately 600 light years away, and has a diameter that measures somewhere between 500 times and 950 times that of our own Sun. This uncertainty is down to the star's nature – it is a red supergiant at the end of its life.

Stars are long-lived thermonuclear reactors. They spend most of their life fusing hydrogen to helium in a continuous process to generate heat and light. It is the reason why stars shine. But when that hydrogen runs out stars cool and expand. They cast off tenuous layers of gas into space, becoming bigger and brighter in the process. This is what is happening on Betelgeuse at the moment, and so getting a precise fix on its size is tricky.

In a telescope Betelgeuse is a deep orange colour and looks fantastic against the darkness of Exmoor's sky. The real fascination though is what *could* happen to Betelgeuse as early as tonight. Being a massive star in the latter stages of its life its light is being maintained only by burning helium into carbon and later carbon into heavier elements until the core contains mostly iron. It is right at this point that nuclear fusion ceases, and the star as we know it essentially dies.

Since energy is no longer being radiated from the core, in less than a second, the star begins gravitational collapse. When this happens the core temperature increases to over 100 billion degrees almost instantaneously as iron atoms at the star's centre are crushed together. At the same time the repulsive force between nuclei overcomes the force of gravity, and the core recoils out from the heart of the star in a shock wave, which we see as a supernova explosion.

We have no idea how far into the helium-burning or carbon-burning stage Betelgeuse is. If it's close to the end that core collapse could be imminent. My advice is to keep watching Betelgeuse. If it blows you'll know about it as the resulting supernova explosion could be spectacular, rivalling the brightness of the full moon for a couple of weeks or more.

Double and Multiple Star Systems

It is estimated that of all of the stars in our galaxy as many as 80% of them are binary star systems. Unlike our Sun, which is a single star, a binary star system consists of two or more stars that are gravitationally bound, and so are in orbit around each other, or more correctly in orbit around a common centre of mass. To the naked eye binary stars often appear as a single star. It is not until you turn binoculars or a telescope to them that the single star is split into a double or multiple star system. Sometimes the stars in a system are so dim and so close together that they can't be separated out visually. Spectroscopic analysis of the star's light is instead used to reveal these *invisible* members, as well as the star's chemical composition, its mass and radius.

Artistic rendition of a triple star system as seen from a hypothetical moon orbiting the Jupiter-sized exoplanet HD 188753Ab, 149-light years away in the constellation of Cygnus.
NASA

Additional to these true binary stars we can also see *optical binaries*. These are two or more stars that appear close together in the sky from our viewing position on Exmoor, yet in reality they are many light years away from each other with no gravitational link. Essentially, what we are seeing here is an optical illusion, but they're still fun to track down in a telescope.

Binary Star System
Two stars orbiting around a common centre of mass

Binary stars orbit a common centre of mass. If one star in the system is more massive than the other then the centre of mass will be closer to the bigger star

Common centre of mass

Observing Double and Multiple Stars

There are enough bright double and multiple star systems in our galaxy to make binary star hunting an all-year-round stargazing activity from Exmoor. All you need is a small telescope and some star maps to help you work out where to look.

Top 10 Double Stars from Exmoor

DOUBLE STAR	DESCRIPTION	CONSTELLATION	MIN. EQUIPMENT	VISIBLE
Albireo	Gold / Blue	Cygnus	15x70 binoculars	Summer
Castor	Dazzling White Pair	Gemini	90mm telescope	Winter
Mizar-Alcor	Naked Eye Double	Ursa Major	Naked eye	All Year
Epsilon Lyrae	Quadruple System	Lyra	102mm telescope	Summer
Alpha Herculis	Orange / Yellow-green	Hercules	90mm telescope	Summer
Cor Caroli	White-blue / Yellow-white	Canes Venatici	60mm telescope	Spring
Algieba	Deep Yellow Pair	Leo	60mm telescope	Spring
Lambda Orionis	Close White Double	Orion	102mm telescope	Winter
Polaris	Pole Star Double	Ursa Minor	70mm telescope	All Year
Gamma Delphini	Quadruple with Struve 2725	Delphinus	90mm telescope	Autumn

Winter and Spring

Winter and springtime skies are graced by the presence of Castor (Alpha Geminorium). Castor is the seventeenth brightest star in Exmoor's night sky, and is the second brightest star in the constellation of Gemini – the Twins. At 51 light years from Exmoor Castor appears to the naked eye and in binoculars as a single bright white point of light. But turn a telescope with a minimum 90mm aperture to it and your eyes will be greeted by two sparkling white gems of light packed in so close together that you'll see only a slim slither of darkness between them.

These two stars – we'll call them Castor A and Castor B – take 445 years to orbit one another, and are separated physically by nearly 15 billion kilometres. It's a very close association when you consider that the next closest star to our

Castor is a mesmerising sight in telescopes with an aperture larger than 90mm.

Sketch by Seb Jay

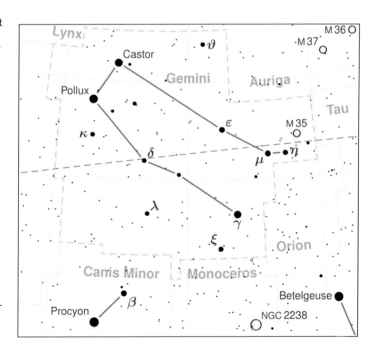

Castor is easy to find in the constellation of Gemini.

Torsten Bronger

own Sun is Alpha Centauri at 4.3 light years away, which is equivalent to 40 trillion kilometres distance.

For sure Castor A and B are a spectacular sight in a telescope, but it's not all that you can see of the Castor system. A little way out from the bright white double is a fainter yellow star. This is YY Geminorium, also known as Castor C. It too is in orbit around Castor A and Castor B making a visual triple star system.

The Castor story in fact goes further as all three stars are themselves spectroscopic doubles, making a total of six members in the star system, all in orbit around one another!

Viewing Challenge:
Easy to see
Equipment: Telescope
Best Views: All year round. See table of top 10 double stars from Exmoor.
Photography Tips: A camera held up to the eyepiece of a telescope will capture the brighter and wider double star pairings. Use a high ISO setting. Higher quality images, and photos of fainter double star systems, are best taken with a camera or webcam mounted to a telescope, which is itself attached to a motorised equatorial mount.

Summer and Autumn

Overhead on summer nights and early autumn evenings is the constellation of Cygnus, the Swan. Its outstretched wings dominate the upper left area of the Summer Triangle, the swan's long neck and head reaching down towards the Triangle's centre. Just right of centre in the Triangle is the relatively bright 3rd magnitude star Albireo. It forms the swan's head, and to the naked eye appears as a fairly insignificant star. In a telescope it's a different story. The star transforms into a majestic double star of golden yellow and sapphire blue light. Both sparkle brightly, the pair being separated by a good chunk of space, making them an easy catch.

With its gold and blue star pairing Albireo in the constellation of Cygnus is regarded as one of the most spectacular double stars in the northern hemisphere sky.
Dietmar Hager

Knowing the relationship between the two stars adds to Albireo's fascination. Both stars are 380 light years from Earth and orbit each other very slowly over a period of around 75,000 years. The primary member of the pairing – the brighter golden yellow star – is a cool giant some 50 times larger than the Sun, and more than 950 times more luminous. The fainter blue star is a much hotter and smaller dwarf star. It spins extremely rapidly, making a full rotation in just over half an Earth day.

Star Birth

Stellar Nurseries

IN EXMOOR'S DARK sky we can see stars being born. Huge stellar nurseries reveal themselves as misty patches of light across the heavens. Some we can see with the naked eye, others only with binoculars or a telescope.

Stars form from dense clouds of cold interstellar gas and dust. The clouds coalesce under gravity, heating up as hydrogen atoms pack together ever more tightly. It's a cyclical process. The bigger the cloud becomes the greater its gravitational pull, and so the more mass it attracts and the hotter it gets. Move on a few tens of thousands of years and what we have is a dense sphere of material

Opposite: The Great Orion Nebula (Messier 42) is visible from Exmoor during the autumn, winter and spring.
Dave Eagle

Below: Located more than 7,000 light years away the Eagle Nebula (Messier 16) is easy to spot under Exmoor's dark sky in a telescope.
Dave Eagle

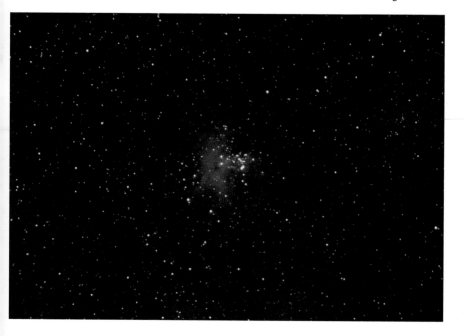

Top 10 Stellar Nurseries and Star Clusters

OBJECT	DESCRIPTION	CONSTELLATION	MIN. EQUIPMENT	VISIBLE
Messier 42	Orion Nebula	Orion	10x50 binoculars	Winter
Messier 17	Swan Nebula	Sagittarius	10x50 binoculars	Summer
Messier 16	Eagle Nebula	Serpens	15x70 binoculars	Summer
Messier 8	Lagoon Nebula	Sagittarius	10x50 binoculars	Summer
Messier 20	Trifid Nebula	Sagittarius	60mm telescope	Summer
Messier 45	Pleiades	Taurus	10x50 binoculars	Autumn
Messier 11	Wild Duck Cluster	Scutum	10x50 binoculars	Summer
Messier 44	Beehive Cluster	Cancer	10x50 binoculars	Spring
NGC 864/869	Perseus Double Cluster	Perseus	10x50 binoculars	All Year
NGC 457	Owl Cluster	Cassiopeia	60mm telescope	All Year

Top 10 stellar nurseries and star clusters visible from Exmoor.

with an internal temperature approaching up to ten million degrees Celsius. That's hot enough for hydrogen fusion to begin. When it does the sphere ignites in a nuclear reaction that produces helium and vast amounts of energy to create a new star. It is the immense heat from these new stars that lights up the surrounding stellar nursery gas clouds, sometimes making them glow in the visual spectrum, and so allowing us to see them from Exmoor's dark sky.

Observing Stellar Nurseries

The Great Orion Nebula in the constellation of Orion is a gigantic stellar nursery 1,500 light years away. It is easy to find in the winter sky. Look towards the south in the evening to locate Orion using the star maps in this book. You'll see three bright stars in a row running across the centre of the constellation. This is Orion's belt. Dropping down from the belt on the left-hand side is a line of fainter stars. This is Orion's sword, and it is here where we find the Great Orion Nebula, visible as a small misty patch of light to the naked eye.

Turn binoculars or a small telescope to the nebula and the view is simply breathtaking. The misty patch resolves into a highly structured cloud of ionized hydrogen gas. Bright and dark filaments can be traced around the cloud, and embedded near its centre is a tightly packed cluster of newborn stars known as the *Trapezium*.

In the summer sky more stellar nurseries are on show. The Swan Nebula in the constellation of Sagittarius is an immensely large star-forming region thought to be about 15 light years in diameter, and located some 5,000 to 6,000 light years from Earth. From Exmoor it reveals itself only in binoculars or a telescope, taking on the appearance of a swan in profile, with its long neck curving up around to its graceful head.

The Eagle Nebula in the constellation of Serpens is another distant star-forming region visible in the summer sky. This one is more than 7,000 light years away. Its light is more subtle than the Swan's, but it still makes for a wonderful view through a telescope on a moonless night from Exmoor. When the Hubble Space Telescope turned its attention to the Eagle Nebula it imaged the 'Pillars of Creation' – a photograph that has gone on to become one of the most famous space shots of all time.

This stellar nursery takes on the appearance of a swan in profile. The shape is easy to make out photographically and visually from a dark sky. Dave Eagle.

The Pillars of Creation reveal dark towering fingers of star-forming gas and dust, inside which new stars are being formed.
NASA / ESA

Star Clusters

Stars emit a constant flow of highly charged particles, mainly protons and electrons, from their upper atmospheres throughout their lives. From our Sun we call this the solar wind. From other stars we call it a stellar wind.

Newborn stars are thought to have fierce stellar winds consisting of ultra high-energy particles travelling out into space at super-

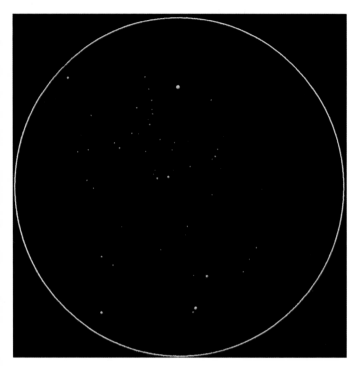

Many thousands of small star clusters are found across Exmoor's dark sky with a telescope.
Sketch by Seb Jay

Viewing Challenge: Easy to see
Equipment: Eyes / Binoculars /Telescope
Best Views: All year round. See table of top 10 stellar nurseries and star clusters from Exmoor.
Photography Tips: A camera mounted on a tripod with a telephoto lens can be used to capture a widefield view of the brighter stellar nurseries and star clusters. Use a wide aperture and high ISO. More detailed image captures require a camera or webcam mounted on a telescope, which is itself attached to a motorised equatorial mount.

sonic speeds. The wind, quite literally, blows away the interstellar gas and dust out of which the stars were born, dispersing it across interstellar space. Left behind are the stars themselves, gathered into clusters that range in size from 4 to 5 stars to 1,000 or more.

Observing Star Clusters

The Pleiades or Seven Sisters is among the most celebrated of the many thousands of star clusters that populate our galaxy. It actually consists of about 10 hot blue-white stars that can easily be seen with the naked eye from Exmoor on a moonless night, plus a larger number of fainter stars visible only in binoculars and telescopes. The cluster is about 425 light years away from Earth, and is about 100 million years old – quite young in galactic terms. Most of the stars in the cluster are many times larger and more luminous than our own Sun, so much so that their starlight faintly illuminates a nearby interstellar gas cloud, which can sometimes be seen from Exmoor in binoculars or a telescope around the star Merope.

Overleaf: Messier 45, the Pleiades Star Cluster, is easy to spot with the naked eye on autumn and winter evenings.
Dave Eagle

83

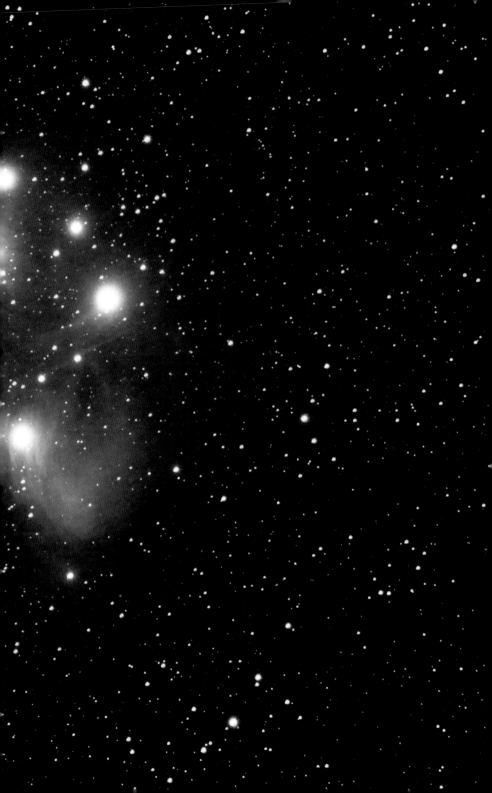

Messier 44,
the Beehive
Cluster, is a
striking sight
in spring skies.
Dean Salman

In the spring sky we have Praesepe or the Beehive Cluster in the constellation of Cancer. It is roughly the same distance from Earth as the Pleiades, but is much older with an age of 600 million years. From Exmoor on a moonless night the Beehive appears as a misty patch of light to the naked eye. Binoculars and telescopes reveal a tangled mass of mostly blue-white stars intermingling with several hundred fainter stars, plus a small number of red giants – two of which are very obvious as bright yellow-orange stars in the cluster. Among the fainter stars in the Beehive are two with the designation Pr0201 and Pr02011. In 2012 both were found to have a planet orbiting them. Both stars can be seen through a telescope from Exmoor.

Planetary Nebula and White Dwarfs

Stars that have evolved into red giants are near the end of their stellar lives. What becomes of them is very much down to their size. Red giants that are up to eight times the size of our Sun are destined to collapse under gravity to leave a dense mass of electrons all crushed together into a sphere about the size of the Earth. These spheres are called white dwarfs. They are basically the exposed dying hearts of stars and start immensely hot, shining brightly. Over tens of thousands of years they fade as their heat is lost, cooling into giant lumps of invisible carbon – a black dwarf.

In the transformation process between red giant and white dwarf the dying star casts off its envelope of stellar gases. The heat from the white dwarf ionizes this gas envelope, illuminating it as the

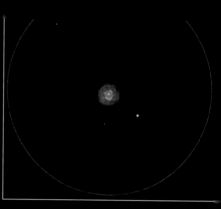

The Eskimo Nebula reveals a lot of structure in large telescopes at high magnification. Sketch by Seb Jay

Top 10 planetary nebulae visible from Exmoor

Top 10 Planetary Nebulae from Exmoor

OBJECT	DESCRIPTION	CONSTELLATION	MIN. EQUIPMENT	VISIBLE
Messier 57	Ring Nebula	Lyra	70mm telescope	Summer
Messier 27	Dumbbell Nebula	Vulpecula	70mm telescope	Summer
Messier 97	Owl Nebula	Ursa Major	90mm telescope	All Year
Messier 76	Little Dumbbell Nebula	Perseus	90mm telescope	Autumn
NGC 7662	Blue Snowball Nebula	Andromeda	90mm telescope	Autumn
NGC 2392	Eskimo Nebula	Gemini	102mm telescope	Winter
NGC 6543	Cat's Eye Nebula	Draco	60mm telescope	All Year
NGC 7293	Helix Nebula	Aquarius	15x70 binoculars	Autumn
NGC 3242	Ghost of Jupiter Nebula	Hydra	90mm telescope	Spring
NGC 6826	Blinking Planetary Nebula	Cygnus	90mm telescope	Summer

Messier 27, the ghostly dumbbell nebula, hangs in the sky in the constellation of Vulpecula inside the Summer Triangle. A small telescope under Exmoor's dark sky reveals the apple-core shape.
Dave Eagle

gas speeds outwards into interstellar space. The result is what we know to be a planetary nebula like the Ring Nebula, Eskimo Nebula and Dumbbell Nebula. Many of these planetary nebulae are visible from Exmoor with a telescope. If the telescope is large enough you can even see the white dwarf at the nebula's centre.

Messier 57, the Ring Nebula, is an easy catch in a small telescope from Exmoor. Photographs reveal the white dwarf at the nebula's centre.
Dave Eagle

Supernovae, Neutron Stars and Black Holes

Massive stars that are at least 20 to 25 times larger than our Sun undergo a dramatic core collapse at the end of their lives. Their stellar material is ejected into interstellar space at supersonic speeds in a bright supernova explosion. What is left behind is a neutron star instead of a white dwarf. Neutron stars are so dense that electrons are crushed into the nucleus of their atoms. The electrons combine with protons to form neutrons, essentially rendering neutron stars as single gigantic atomic nuclei.

Very few neutron stars exist in our galaxy and we cannot see them directly from Exmoor. We only see the gaseous remnants left over from the supernova explosion. One such remnant is the Crab Nebula in the constellation of Taurus.

In the summer of 1054 Chinese and Japanese astronomers saw a new star in the sky. It shone brighter than Venus, and was easily seen in the daytime sky for more than 3 weeks. At night the new star remained a beacon of light in the heavens, close to the star Zeta Tauri, for more than a year.

Fast forward nearly a thousand years. We now know that the new star was a supernova explosion in our own galaxy. Where the star once existed we see an expanding mesh of interstellar material that is still rushing out into space at 4.8 million kilometres per hour. This growing nebulous mass is called the Crab Nebula, and appears as a small patch of misty mottled light in binoculars and telescopes at the very same location of the supernova. Embedded within the material is a super-dense neutron star about the size of a small town and spinning at an incredible 30 times per second.

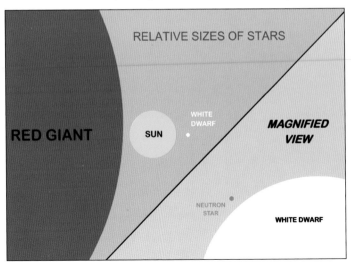

Stars change size as they evolve. The graphic compares the Sun to the size of a solar mass star as a red giant, and then as a white dwarf. The size of a neutron star is also shown against a magnified view of a white dwarf.

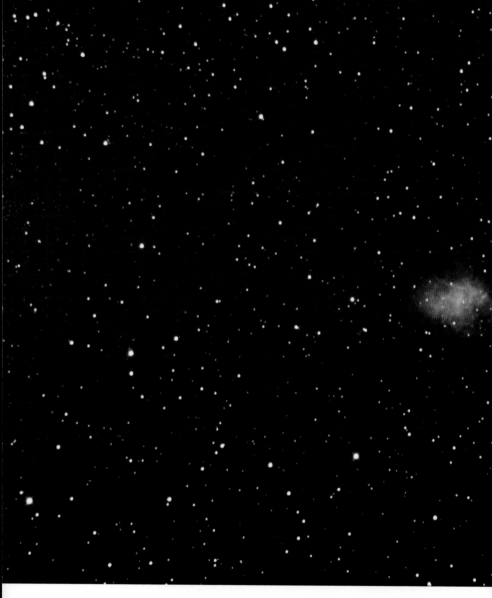

Supergiants like Betelgeuse that are more than 25 times the mass of our own Sun also explode as supernovae at the end of their lives. Being so much larger the dense core left behind is bigger, so big in fact that gravity crushes its neutrons out of existence to form a black hole.

By their very nature we cannot see black holes as nothing can escape from them – not even light. What we can see is their

Messier 1, the Crab Nebula, is visible in small telescopes as an 's' shaped patch of light. Larger telescopes reveal structure in the nebula. Dave Eagle

effect on neighbouring stars. Visible in 100mm aperture telescopes 6,000 light years from Exmoor is a blue supergiant star in the constellation of Cygnus known as HDE 226868. It orbits an unseen companion, presumed to be a 15-solar mass black hole. We can see the star, and can only imagine chunks of it being ripped off and consumed by the fast-spinning black hole in orbit next to it.

Globular Clusters - The Most Distant Objects in our Galaxy

RANGING FROM 25,000 light years in distance to more than 300,000 light years away are some of the most enigmatic sights in Exmoor's night sky. Globular clusters are curious spherical masses, each containing anywhere between a few thousand stars to upwards of half a million. They swarm around the galaxy in random orbits of many hundreds of millions of years, occupying a region of space known as the galactic halo.

The galactic halo extends outwards for tens of thousands of light years in all directions from the spiral plane of the Milky Way. It's a region of space we know little about, and is thought to be mostly

Messier 13, the Great Hercules Globular Cluster, is one of the most spectacular sights in the night sky from Exmoor. This sketch was made at the eyepiece of a small telescope. Larger telescopes reveal individual stars in the cluster.
Owain John

N

W

2320-2340 BST, 23rd April 2013
Bright moonlight, hazy cloud

Skyliner 200P Super 25
48x

made up of ancient dark matter, possibly the cores of long dead stars, that we cannot see – relics of the galaxy's formation more than 13 billion years ago. In amongst this debris are our globular clusters. They are very old. Most are thought to be as old as the galaxy itself and contain ancient stars more than three times the age of our Sun.

One hundred and fifty eight globular clusters are known. No one yet knows why they are there in the galactic halo, or how they formed. What we do know is that the stars in the cluster are all gravitationally bound, so remain together through their lifetimes.

The Messier 3 Globular Cluster is partially resolved in a 200mm aperture telescope.
Hunter Wilson

Observing Globular Clusters

A lot of globular clusters are easy to track down with binoculars and telescopes. One is even visible to the naked eye on a moonless

Top 10 Globular Clusters from Exmoor

OBJECT	DISTANCE	CONSTELLATION	MIN. EQUIPMENT	VISIBLE
Messier 13	25,000 light years	Hercules	Naked eye	Summer
Messier 3	33,900 light years	Canes Venatici	10x50 binoculars	Spring
Messier 5	24,500 light years	Serpens	10x50 binoculars	Spring
Messier 92	26,700 light years	Hercules	10x50 binoculars	Summer
Messier 15	33,600 light years	Pegasus	10x50 binoculars	Autumn
Messier 79	41,400 light years	Lepus	60mm telescope	Winter
Messier 53	58,000 light years	Coma Berenices	60mm telescope	Spring
Messier 4	7,200 light years	Scorpio	60mm telescope	Summer
Messier 56	32,900 light years	Lyra	90mm telescope	Summer
NGC 2419	300,000 light years	Lynx	150mm telescope	Winter

night from Exmoor. Their random distribution across the night sky makes them accessible all year round. Use the table to find those that are visible in your sky tonight, then use the star maps in this book to track them down.

A 150mm telescope using a moderate or high magnification eyepiece will partially resolve some of the clusters into individual stars. Telescopes with apertures upwards of 300mm will more fully resolve the brighter clusters into many thousands of individual stars. In some globular clusters you can even resolve chains of stars and see mini clusters of stars within the clusters themselves!

Our Local Galaxy Group

Our galaxy is not alone in the Universe. There are many billions of other galaxies spread across time and space. Many are larger than the Milky Way, and tens of millions are smaller. Advances in cosmology over the last century have shown us that galaxies are not randomly distributed. Instead they form groups or clusters of galaxies. The closest galaxy group to Earth is called the Local Group. It comprises 54 galaxies, including our own Milky Way as the group's second largest member.

The Andromeda Galaxy

Located 2.5 million light years from Earth the Andromeda Galaxy (Messier 31) is the largest and brightest member of the Local Group. Like the Milky Way it is a spiral galaxy containing hundreds of billions of stars, and all of the other types of celestial objects we find inside our own galaxy including stellar nurseries, star clusters, planetary nebula, black holes, and quite possibly planets.

From Exmoor we can see this distant *island universe* without any optical equipment. On a moonless night it appears as an elongated smudge of light in the constellation of Andromeda, a short distance above the star Mirach. It is the brightest object we can see in the northern hemisphere night sky that is *outside* our own galaxy, and the second most distant object we can see with the naked eye.

Opposite: Top 10 globular clusters to view from Exmoor

Overleaf: Messier 31, the Andromeda Galaxy, is 2.5 million light years away and moving towards us. In 3 to 4 billion years time it will collide with our own Milky Way galaxy. Dave Eagle

95

Binoculars or a small telescope reveal a mesmerising sight under Exmoor's dark sky. Because the sky is so dark the full extent of the galaxy's size becomes visible. It is huge, stretching more than three times the width of the full moon across the heavens. Getting it all into the same field of view is a challenge!

Messier 33, the Triangulum Galaxy, is 2.9 million light years from Earth. It is the most distant object you can see on Exmoor without binoculars or a telescope.
Dave Eagle

The Triangulum Galaxy

Third behind the Andromeda Galaxy and the Milky Way in terms of galaxy size in the Local Group is the Triangulum Galaxy (Messier 33). At 2.9 million light years from Earth it is more distant than the Andromeda Galaxy, but is arguably more photogenic as its spiral arms are almost face-on to Earth.

On a moonless night under Exmoor's dark sky the Triangulum Galaxy is just visible to the naked eye as an indistinct patch of faint grey light in the constellation of Triangulum, a little way below the star Mirach in Andromeda. It's not a view you'll see from a town or city for sure. It really is only Exmoor's dark sky that makes it possible for us to see this distant galaxy with the naked eye. As such, the Triangulum Galaxy ranks as the most distant object visible from Exmoor that can be seen without the use of binoculars or a telescope.

With a telescope the view is awe-inspiring. Let your eyes fully adapt to the dark and you'll see a ghostly disc of light resolve into brighter spiral arms separated by darker lanes in instruments of 150mm aperture and larger. Telescopes of 250mm aperture will start to show some of this distant galaxy's stellar nurseries (HII regions), the most notable one having a designation of NGC 604.

> **Viewing Challenge:** Easy to see
> **Equipment:** Eyes / Binoculars / Telescope
> **Best Views:** Early autumn to early spring
> **Photography Tips:** A camera or webcam mounted on a telescope, which is itself fixed to a motorised equatorial mount is the best way to image the brighter members of our local galaxy group. Several images need to be taken and then stacked together in image processing software to obtain a high-detailed view.

The Virgo Galaxy Cluster

Beyond the Local Group we have to travel an extraordinary 50 million light years through space and time to reach the next Group. The Virgo Galaxy Cluster contains more than 1,200 galaxies stretching some 15 million light years across the Universe. Spiral galaxies like the Milky Way intermingle with tiny dwarf galaxies and giant elliptical galaxies, the biggest of which is nearly five times the size of the Milky Way. Each galaxy contains billions of stars, the largest ones being made up of several hundred billion stars. Inside each we'll find many of the same features as we see in our own Milky Way.

As amazing as it might seem, even at this extraordinary distance, several hundred of these galaxies in the Virgo Cluster can be seen with small portable telescopes on a dark night from Exmoor. Let's just think about this for a moment. We're talking about seeing light that is older than the Himalayan Mountain Range; light that pre-dates the existence of humans by many millions of years, and goes back to a time when the Arctic was a warm and wet swamp. That light is still moving at nothing less than the speed of light, and all we have to do is point a telescope in the direction of the constellation of Virgo in the springtime sky to see it.

Top 10 galaxies to view from Exmoor.

Top 10 Galaxies from Exmoor

OBJECT	DISTANCE	CONSTELLATION	MIN. EQUIPMENT	VISIBLE
Andromeda Galaxy	2.5 million light years	Andromeda	Naked eye	Autumn
Triangulum Galaxy	2.9 million light years	Triangulum	Naked eye	Autumn
Messier 81 / 82	11.8 million light years	Ursa Major	10x50 binoculars	All Year
Black Eye Galaxy	20 million light years	Coma Berenices	90mm telescope	Spring
Sombrero Galaxy	50 million light years	Virgo	90mm telescope	Spring
Messier 65 / 66	35 million light years	Leo	90mm telescope	Spring
Whirlpool Galaxy	27 million light years	Canes Venatici	90mm telescope	All Year
Pinwheel Galaxy	25 million light years	Ursa Major	90mm telescope	All Year
Messier 87	50 million light years	Virgo	90mm telescope	Spring
NGC 4874 / 4889	320 million light years	Coma Berenices	200mm telescope	Spring

Messier 87 is a giant elliptical galaxy some 50 million light years from Earth. It is an easy catch in a small or medium-sized telescope under Exmoor's dark sky.
NASA / Hubble Space Telescope

Observing the Virgo Galaxy Cluster

The Virgo Galaxy Cluster is best seen in the evening sky between February and May. Telescopes with at least a 150mm aperture are needed to pull out the brightest members, which are all located in a 10-degree patch of sky between the star Epsilon Virgo (Vindemiatrix) and Beta Leonis (Denebola) in the constellation of Leo. Telescopes of 200mm to 250mm aperture reveal hundreds of galaxies in the group, including spirals, ellipticals and dwarf galaxies. Larger telescopes reveal delicate structure in a number of the galaxies. Some people have even glimpsed the mysterious 5,000 light- year-long jet of superheated gas that is being ejected from the core of the Messier 87 (M87) Galaxy at close to the speed of light.

A wide-field view of the Virgo Galaxy Cluster. The black dots are where bright foreground stars have been blacked out. Chris Mihos (Case Western Reserve University)/ESO

NGC 4565 is an edge-on spiral galaxy 40 million light years from Earth in the direction of the Virgo Cluster. Sketch by Seb Jay

Messier 88 Spiral Galaxy in the Virgo Cluster imaged using the 24-inch Telescope on Mt Lemmon in Arizona, USA. J Schulman

The Coma Galaxy Cluster

Want more of a challenge? Okay, let's push out to 320 million light years distance to find the Coma Galaxy Cluster. Visible to telescopes with apertures larger than 200mm the Coma Cluster consists of more than 1,000 spiral, elliptical and dwarf galaxies occupying a small patch of sky between the stars Beta Coma Berenices and 31 Coma Berenices, slightly above the Virgo Constellation, and to the left of the grouping of stars known as the Hair of Berenices.

The two giant elliptical galaxies of NGC 4889 and NGC 4874 dominate the cluster. They are so large and bright that even out at 320 million light years from Earth we can see them with a 200mm telescope from Exmoor's International Dark Sky Reserve. Larger telescopes reveal several other galaxies in the cluster – quite a feat when you consider that the light you're seeing is almost as old as the rocks you're standing on, and pre-dates all mammal life on Earth.

Wide field view of the Coma Galaxy Cluster from the 32-inch Telescope at Mt Lemmon in Arizona, USA. Adam Block/ Mount Lemmon SkyCenter/ University of Arizona

Quasar 3C 273

How far can you see with a portable telescope from Exmoor? As far as Quasar 3C 273 is the answer! Located an astounding 2.5 billion light years from Earth Quasar 3C 273 is an extremely distant galaxy being consumed by a supermassive black hole at its centre that is more than a billion times the mass of our own Sun. This extragalactic feast generates a gargantuan amount of energy and light, so much so that the feasting act outshines the host galaxy by more than a hundredfold. That's bright enough for 3C 273 to be visible in telescopes of 200mm aperture and more under Exmoor's dark sky.

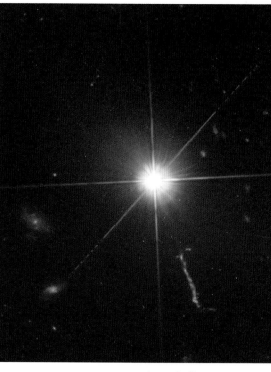

Image Credit NASA/ESA and J. Bahcall (IAS)

The Quasar is located in the constellation of Virgo, slightly above the star Gamma Virgo (Porrima), and not far from the star Eta Virgo. You'll need a decent star chart to find it, and even then it'll be tricky to identify as it just looks like a dim star. It's worth tracking down though, as it's as close as we can get to seeing a black hole through a telescope. There's also the added fascination that the light you're seeing has travelled for more than half the Earth's life to reach your eyes!

Viewing Challenge: Difficult
Equipment: 200mm aperture telescope (minimum requirement)
Event Frequency: Occasional
Best Views: February to May
Photography Tips: A camera or webcam mounted on a telescope, which is itself fixed to a motorised equatorial mount is the best way to image 3C 273. Several images need to be taken and then stacked together in image processing software to obtain a high-detailed view.

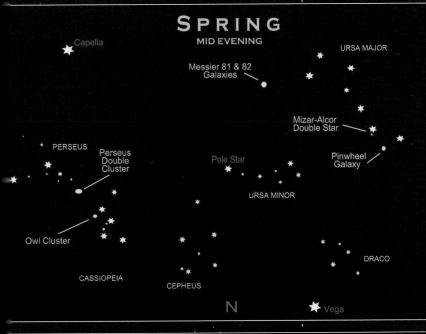

SPRING
MID EVENING

Capella

URSA MAJOR

Messier 81 & 82
Galaxies

Mizar-Alcor
Double Star

PERSEUS

Perseus
Double
Cluster

Pole Star

Pinwheel
Galaxy

URSA MINOR

Owl Cluster

DRACO

CASSIOPEIA

CEPHEUS

N

Vega

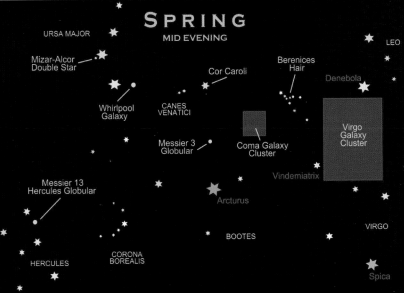

SPRING
MID EVENING

URSA MAJOR

LEO

Mizar-Alcor
Double Star

Cor Caroli

Berenices
Hair

Denebola

Whirlpool
Galaxy

CANES
VENATICI

Virgo
Galaxy
Cluster

Messier 3
Globular

Coma Galaxy
Cluster

Vindemiatrix

Messier 13
Hercules Globular

Arcturus

VIRGO

BOOTES

HERCULES

CORONA
BOREALIS

Spica

E

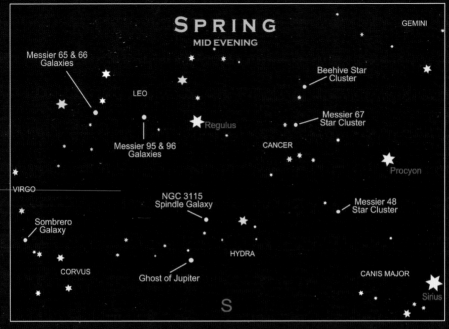

SPRING
MID EVENING

GEMINI

Messier 65 & 66
Galaxies

Beehive Star
Cluster

LEO

Messier 67
Star Cluster

Regulus

CANCER

Messier 95 & 96
Galaxies

Procyon

VIRGO

NGC 3115
Spindle Galaxy

Messier 48
Star Cluster

Sombrero
Galaxy

HYDRA

CORVUS

Ghost of Jupiter

CANIS MAJOR

Sirius

S

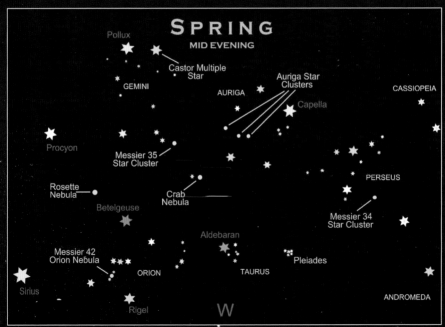

SPRING
MID EVENING

Pollux

Castor Multiple
Star

GEMINI

AURIGA

Auriga Star
Clusters

CASSIOPEIA

Capella

Procyon

Messier 35
Star Cluster

PERSEUS

Rosette
Nebula

Crab
Nebula

Betelgeuse

Messier 34
Star Cluster

Messier 42
Orion Nebula

Aldebaran

Pleiades

ORION

TAURUS

Sirius

Rigel

ANDROMEDA

W

105

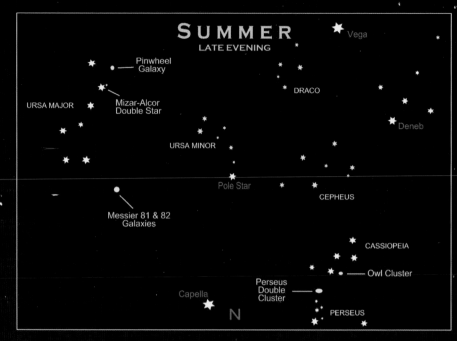

SUMMER
LATE EVENING

Vega

Pinwheel Galaxy

DRACO

Mizar-Alcor Double Star

URSA MAJOR

Deneb

URSA MINOR

Pole Star

CEPHEUS

Messier 81 & 82 Galaxies

CASSIOPEIA

Owl Cluster

Perseus Double Cluster

Capella

PERSEUS

N

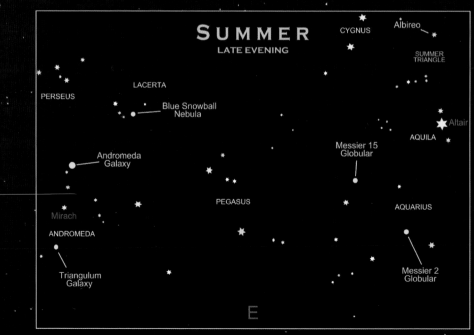

SUMMER
LATE EVENING

CYGNUS

Albireo

SUMMER TRIANGLE

PERSEUS

LACERTA

Blue Snowball Nebula

Altair

AQUILA

Andromeda Galaxy

Messier 15 Globular

PEGASUS

AQUARIUS

Mirach

ANDROMEDA

Messier 2 Globular

Triangulum Galaxy

E

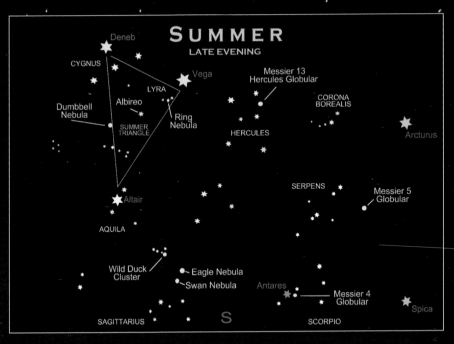

SUMMER
LATE EVENING

Deneb

CYGNUS

Vega

LYRA

Albireo

Dumbbell
Nebula

SUMMER
TRIANGLE

Ring
Nebula

Messier 13
Hercules Globular

CORONA
BOREALIS

HERCULES

Arcturus

Altair

AQUILA

SERPENS

Messier 5
Globular

Wild Duck
Cluster

Eagle Nebula

Swan Nebula

Antares

Messier 4
Globular

Spica

SAGITTARIUS

S

SCORPIO

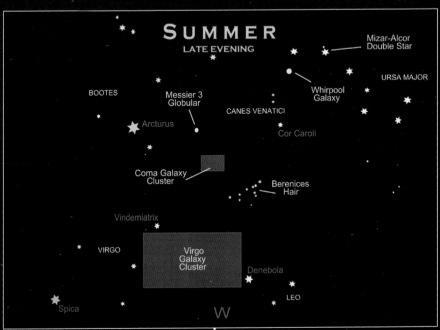

SUMMER
LATE EVENING

Mizar-Alcor
Double Star

URSA MAJOR

Whirlpool
Galaxy

BOOTES

Messier 3
Globular

CANES VENATICI

Arcturus

Cor Caroli

Coma Galaxy
Cluster

Berenices
Hair

Vindemiatrix

VIRGO

Virgo
Galaxy
Cluster

Denebola

Spica

LEO

W

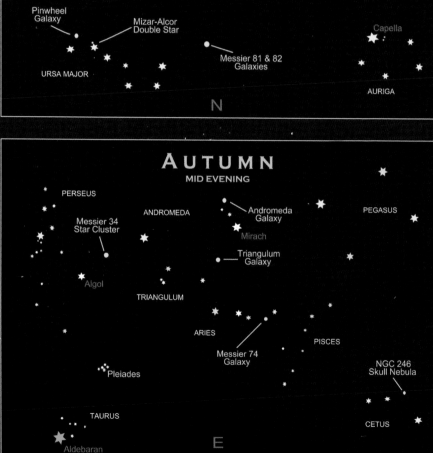

AUTUMN
MID EVENING

CASSIOPEIA

CEPHEUS

Owl Cluster

DRACO

Perseus Double Cluster

URSA MINOR

Pole Star

PERSEUS

Pinwheel Galaxy

Mizar-Alcor Double Star

Capella

Messier 81 & 82 Galaxies

URSA MAJOR

AURIGA

N

AUTUMN
MID EVENING

PERSEUS

ANDROMEDA

Andromeda Galaxy

PEGASUS

Messier 34 Star Cluster

Mirach

Triangulum Galaxy

Algol

TRIANGULUM

ARIES

PISCES

Messier 74 Galaxy

Pleiades

NGC 246 Skull Nebula

TAURUS

CETUS

Aldebaran

E

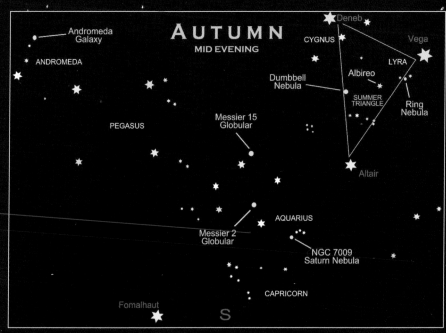

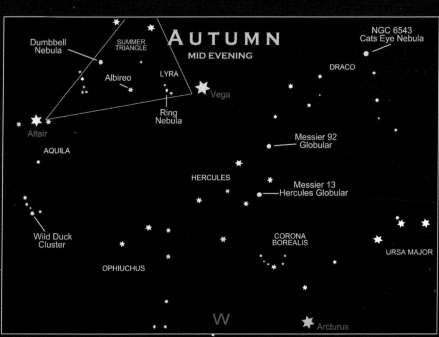

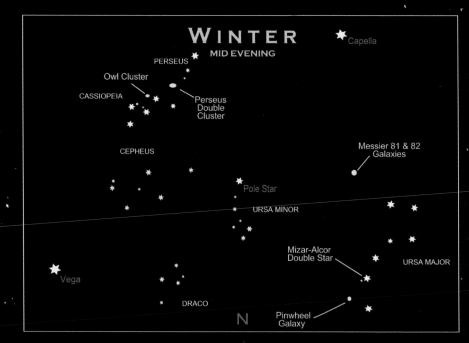

WINTER
MID EVENING

Capella

PERSEUS

Owl Cluster

CASSIOPEIA

Perseus
Double
Cluster

CEPHEUS

Messier 81 & 82
Galaxies

Pole Star

URSA MINOR

Mizar-Alcor
Double Star

URSA MAJOR

Vega

DRACO

Pinwheel
Galaxy

N

WINTER
MID EVENING

URSA MAJOR

Castor
Multiple Star

Messier 35
Star Cluster

GEMINI

Owl Nebula

Pollux

Eskimo
Nebula

Betelgeuse

ORION

Beehive
Star Cluster

Messier 67
Star Cluster

NGC 2903
Galaxy

Procyon

Algieba
Double Star

CANCER

LEO

Regulus

Messier 48
Star Cluster

E

WINTER
MID EVENING

AURIGA

GEMINI

Messier 36+37
Star Clusters

Pleiades

Aldebaran

Crab
Nebula

TAURUS

ARIES

Messier 74
Galaxy

Rosette
Nebula

Betelgeuse

Procyon

ORION

CETUS

Messier 42
Orion Nebula

Rigel

ERIDANUS

Sirius

LEPUS

Messier 79
Globular

Messier 41
Star Cluster

S

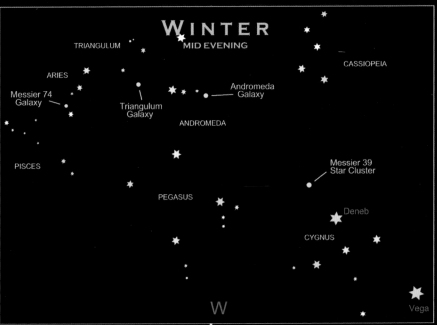

WINTER
MID EVENING

TRIANGULUM

CASSIOPEIA

ARIES

Messier 74
Galaxy

Triangulum
Galaxy

Andromeda
Galaxy

ANDROMEDA

PISCES

Messier 39
Star Cluster

PEGASUS

Deneb

CYGNUS

W

Vega

10 Binoculars and Telescopes

Binoculars

BINOCULARS REVEAL hundreds of more stars than can be seen with the naked eye. Just a good quality pair of 10x50 binoculars is all that is needed to give you some lovely wide field views of the Milky Way in the summer and winter sky. Mounted on a tripod for steadiness you'll get excellent views of the brighter star clusters, nebula and galaxies. In the latter category the likes of the M31 Andromeda Galaxy, and the M81 / M82 galaxy pairing in Ursa Major 11.8 million light years away are easily picked up in 10x50 binoculars from Exmoor.

Binocular Advantages
• Highly portable
• Inexpensive

Binocular Disadvantages
• Difficult to get a steady view when handheld
• Small fixed magnification yields widefield views only

Opposite: The summer Milky Way from a dark sky location.
Image by Peter Truscott.

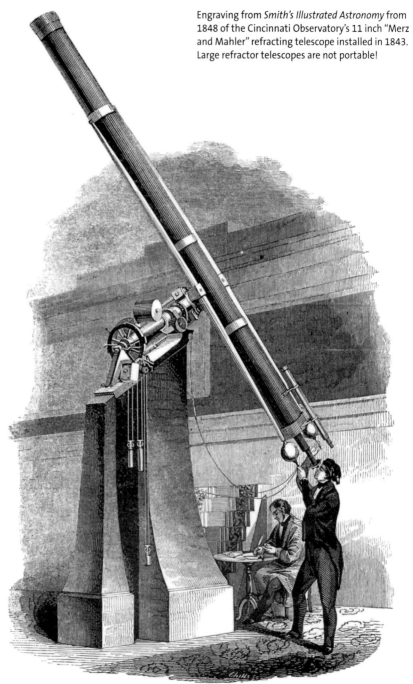

Engraving from *Smith's Illustrated Astronomy* from 1848 of the Cincinnati Observatory's 11 inch "Merz and Mahler" refracting telescope installed in 1843. Large refractor telescopes are not portable!

Refractor Telescopes

Refractors are classic long tube telescopes. An objective lens of one or more optical elements sits at the front aperture of the tube. At the rear the light path comes to a focus, and is magnified according to the eyepiece used. For more comfortable viewing a *diagonal* is placed between the light path and eyepiece to change the light path by 90° to the angle of the tube. This means that you can stand over the back of the tube and look down to view objects through the eyepiece.

Refractor Advantages
• Brightest and sharpest views per cm of aperture
• Optics remain in excellent alignment through the telescope's life

Refractor Disadvantages
• Only portable up to 120mm aperture
• Most expensive telescope per cm of aperture

Small and portable Meade refractor telescope.

Reflector Telescopes

Reflectors are a common design of telescope used by amateur astronomers. Light is captured by a highly reflective primary mirror that sits at the bottom-end of the telescope tube. The mirror is parabolic so that its reflected light is brought inwards to a focus point near the top end of the telescope tube. A small secondary mirror is held at this convergence point, and angled 45-degrees, reflecting the light out to the side of the telescope and up to the viewer's eyepiece. As with refractors different eyepieces can be used to change the magnification and field of view angle.

Reflector Advantages
• Portable to 300mm aperture and easy to set up, especially if using a dobsonian-style mount
• Most inexpensive telescope per cm of aperture

Reflector Disadvantages

- Diagonal mirror and supporting structure reduce image brightness and contrast
- Occasional mirror re-alignment required in telescopes with apertures of 200mm+

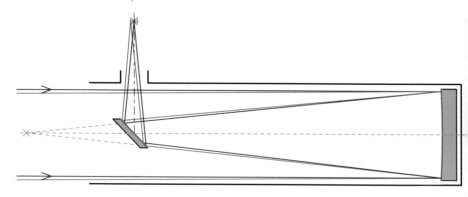

300mm and 200mm aperture reflectors on dobsonian-style mounts.

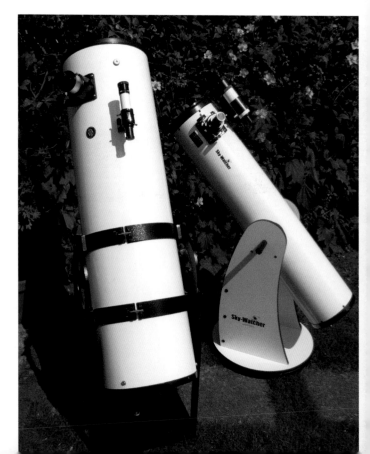

Catadioptric telescopes are short tube telescopes that use both refraction and reflection to deliver an image to the eyepiece. Light enters the telescope through a front glass corrector plate before falling onto a spherical primary mirror at the rear of the tube. The corrector plate *corrects* the light for spherical aberration caused by the design of the primary mirror. What happens next then depends on whether you have a Schmidt-Cassegrain or Maksutov-Cassegrain telescope.

Schmidt-Cassegrains support a convex secondary mirror at the rear of the front corrector plate. This bounces the light from the primary mirror back through the tube, bringing it to a focus at the eyepiece at the back of telescope. Maksutov-Cassegrains use a curved corrective plate at the front, the back of which is mirrored to bounce light down the type to the eyepiece.

Catadioptric Advantages
- Compact and portable up to 300mm aperture
- As the light path is quite long inside the tube a high focal ratio of f/10 to f/15 can be achieved, offering bigger and brighter views than through a reflector

Catadioptric Disadvantages
- Front corrector plate prone to dewing in moist air
- More expensive than a reflector of equal aperture size

Dunkery Beacon & Dunkery Hill *****
RECOMMENDED
Grid Reference: SS 89143 41587
Latitude: 51.162754
Longitude: -3.5867792
Elevation: 520 metres
Views: Exceptional views in all directions.
Location Description: Minor road signposted to Dunkery Beacon. South access from B3224 Wheddon Cross. North access from A39 near Allerford.
Site Description: Dunkery Beacon is the highest point on Exmoor, and is one of the darkest locations in the International Dark Sky Reserve. Closest parking is at Dunkery Gate car park. You then have to ascend an 800-metre rough path up the hillside to the summit. It's an isolated spot. Walking boots and portable telescope / stargazing equipment recommended. More accessible are the half dozen or so roadside pull-ins along the minor road between Dunkery Gate and Webber's Post. They're great spots to set up a telescope with views out eastwards, although you will have occasional passing traffic.

Opposite: Dunkery Beacon looking northwest.

Below: Dunkery Hill looking southeast.

Wimbleball Lake Country Park *****
RECOMMENDED
Grid Reference: SS 96689 30639
Latitude: 51.065754
Longitude: -3.4757617
Elevation: 250 metres
Views: Excellent views in all directions. Exceptional views across the lake with starlight reflecting off the water.
Location Description: Wimbleball Lake is accessible at night via the main entrance for the café and campsite. Access from the north via Blagdon Lane off the B3224. From the northeast and south use the B3190 and turn off towards Redgate and Woolcotts.
Site Description: Wimbleball Lake is an official Dark Sky Discovery Site. It is managed by the South West Lakes Trust and is a flagship dark sky location within Exmoor National Park. The main gates to the site remain open 24/7. Visitors are advised to park in the main car park near the café. There is no access by car to the waterfront after dark. However, telescopes / stargazing equipment can be carried and set-up at the waterfront (five minute walk from the car park). There is unrestricted access to the fields around the lake offering breathtaking views of the stars in all directions and across the lake. Public conveniences available.

Wimbleball Lake looking west.

Webber's Post
looking west.

Webber's Post *****
RECOMMENDED
Grid Reference: SS 90265 43886
Latitude: 51.183634
Longitude: -3.5714389
Elevation: 240 metres
Views: Excellent views west, southwest and north.
Location Description: Spur road off the minor road between Dunkery Beacon and Allerford. South access from B3224 Wheddon Cross. North access from A39 near Allerford.
Site Description: Large National Trust car park area with well maintained crushed hardcore surface. Secluded spot with exceptionally dark sky to the south and west. Gently sloping grass and heath to the south and west. NT car park donation box.

Porlock Common
looking west.

Porlock Common *****
RECOMMENDED
Grid Reference: SS 84914 46036
Latitude: 51.201909
Longitude: -3.6486531
Elevation: 430 metres
Views: Great views in all directions.
Location Description: Several small pull-ins on the minor road to Exford over Porlock Common to the southwest of Whitstone Post. Easy access from the A39 at Whitstone Post.
Site Description: Porlock Common rises gently to a heath plateau within 50 metres of the road. Exposed with great views in all directions with the exception of the northwest, which looks back over the road. Location is mostly unaffected by headlights from occasional passing traffic. Ground easy to navigate and very accessible for setting up a telescope / stargazing equipment.

Brendon Common *****
RECOMMENDED
Grid Reference: SS 75931 45147
Latitude: 51.192039
Longitude: -3.7768627
Elevation: 400 metres
Views: Exceptional views in all directions from one of the darkest places on the International Dark Sky Reserve.
Location Description: Two sizeable and well-maintained car parking areas for up to 20 vehicles next to the B3223 between Lynmouth and Simonsbath just south of Dry Bridge.
Site Description: Open common land with extensive views in all directions. From the car parks the land slopes gently upwards to the east offering an elevated area ideal for setting up telescopes and stargazing equipment. There may be occasional headlight interference from passing traffic on the B3223, although the further upslope you go the less interference there will be.

Brendon Common
looking southwest.

West Anstey Common *****
RECOMMENDED
Grid Reference: SS 84003 29683
Latitude: 51.054735
Longitude: -3.6564208
Elevation: 350 metres
Views: Exceptional view in all directions.
Location Description: Hardcore-surface car park near Anstey Common on Ridge Road (minor road) between Dulverton and Twitchen.
Site Description: Open common land on an extensive ridge with expansive views in all directions. Telescopes can be set up in the open car park area or anywhere along the ridge away from the road.

West Anstey Common looking northwest.

Lucott Cross
looking east.

Lucott Cross ****

Grid Reference: SS 84660 42962
Latitude: 51.174231
Longitude: -3.6513044
Elevation: 460 metres
Views: Great views to the east, northeast, southeast and south.
Location Description: Pull-in car park on the single track road a few yards south of Lucott Cross. North access from A39 at Whitstone Post. South access from Mill Lane at Edgcott near Exford.
Site Description: Small pull-in car park for approximately three vehicles. Gently sloping ground to the east for telescope set-up. Overlooks Nutscale Reservoir. Situation is close to road, so possible occasional interference by headlights from infrequent passing traffic. Sheltered from southwest winds by a line of trees on the other side of the road.

Brendon Two Gates ****

Grid Reference: SS 76528 43243
Latitude: 51.175052
Longitude: -3.7676674
Elevation: 420 metres
Views: Exceptional view east, southeast and northeast.
Location Description: Layby on the B3223 at Brendon Two Gates near Hoar Tor. South access from Simonsbath. North access from A39 at Coombe Park Wood.
Site Description: Open moorland with gentle slope to east. Rough layby along the road for up to eight vehicles. Access to fields to east via low stile and gate. Potential for interference from headlights of infrequent passing traffic. Muddy / boggy during wet winters.

Brendon Two Gates
looking east

Whitstone Post looking east.

Whitstone Post ***
Grid Reference: SS 85595 46299
Latitude: 51.204410
Longitude: -3.6389877
Elevation: 370 metres
Views: Good views northwest, north, northeast and east.
Location Description: Two sizeable car parks on the north side of the A39 to the west of Porlock. Easy access from Porlock after ascending Porlock Hill.
Site Description: Both car parks are large with crushed hardcore surfaces and offer views over the Bristol Channel towards Wales. View low down on northern horizon is hampered by light pollution from the South Wales coastline.

County Gate ****

Grid Reference: SS 79326 48628
Latitude: 51.224047
Longitude: -3.7294747
Elevation: 320 metres
Views: Great views to the west, southwest, south and southeast.
Location Description: Open access car park just off the A39 near Cosgate Hill between Lynmouth and Porlock.
Site Description: Large tarmac car park next to visitor centre overlooking Malmsmead. Ground slopes down to a flatter area beyond the car park. Easy to navigate and good area to set up a telescope. Possible interference from headlights of passing vehicles and other vehicles moving in car park. Public convenience on site.

County Gate looking west.

Holdstone Down ***

Grid Reference: SS 62765 47916
Latitude: 51.213907
Longitude: -3.9662159
Elevation: 280 metres
Views: Great views northeast, north and northwest
Location Description: Small well-maintained car park overlooking the Bristol Channel off a minor road between Combe Martin and Trentishoe.
Site Description: Car park for up to 15 vehicles nestled between Holdstone Down and Trentishoe Down. Ground slopes gently down towards the north making for an excellent area in which to set up a telescope. Possible interference from headlights of occasional traffic from the west, and from traffic moving in the car park. Some light pollution to the north from South Wales coast.

Holdstone Down looking northeast.

Haddon Hill ****

Grid Reference: SS 96912 28501
Latitude: 51.046581
Longitude: -3.4719599
Elevation: 320 metres
Views: Exceptional views north, northwest and northeast
Location Description: Haddon Hill Car Park is situated off the B3190 west of Upton at the south end of Wimbleball Lake.
Site Description: Hardcore-surface car park overlooking Wimbleball Lake. Site is shielded by trees to the west and east. Best views are towards the north over Wimbleball Lake. Public convenience on site.

Haddon Hill looking north.

Landacre Bridge ****

Grid Reference: SS 81533 36071
Latitude: 51.111653
Longitude: -3.6937464
Elevation: 270 metres
Views: Good views in all directions.
Location Description: Car parking area on rough ground close to Landacre Bridge west of Withypool. Access from Landacre Lane. Single track.
Site Description: Rough car parking area for 7 – 10 vehicles. There is ample space to the southwest of the car parking area to set up telescopes / stargazing equipment. There's also an opportunity to stargaze next to the bridge itself. Ground prone to flooding in wet winters. Location is at lowest point in the landscape and so horizons are quite high, especially to the south.

Landacre Bridge
looking west.

Winsford Hill
looking northeast.

Winsford Hill ****
Grid Reference: SS 87839 34155
Latitude: 51.095700
Longitude: -3.6030985
Elevation: 420 metres
Views: Great views in all directions.
Location Description: Small car parking area for four – five vehicles off the B3223 at Winsford Hill between Withypool and Dulverton.
Site Description: Open heath with great views in all directions. Headlights from passing traffic heading uphill from Dulverton will hamper southeast view unless you set up amongst the heather on the south side of the road.

Bossington Hill
looking west.

Bossington Hill ****
Grid Reference: SS 91073 47690
Latitude: 51.217986
Longitude: -3.5610344
Elevation: 270 metres
Views: Excellent views in all directions. Not as dark as some other locations with Minehead and Porlock close by.
Location Description: Large car park next to Bossington Hill and Selworthy Beacon at the end of Hill Road west of Minehead. Access from Higher Town area of Minehead.
Site Description: An easy dark sky site to reach from Minehead. The car park is large and leads to open land for easy set-up of telescopes / stargazing equipment. Short walk up to Bossington Hill or Selworthy Beacon is recommended as you'll be less affected by headlights from cars moving in the car park.

Overleaf:
Bossington Hill
looking northeast.
Adrian Cubitt - ATV
Productions Ltd

Stargazing Safety Tips

A few hours out underneath Exmoor's dark skies is an exhilarating experience. But whether it's your first time out or your hundredth time it's a good idea to take a few precautions to be sure that you don't run into trouble while out on the moors in the dark.

Weather: Being an upland location the weather on Exmoor can be quite different to nearby lowland villages and towns. It can also change quickly (and unexpectedly). Winds tend to be stronger the higher up you are, and there's a tendency for low cloud and fog to form in moist airstreams. Always check the weather forecast for Exmoor National Park ahead of a night on the moors. The Met Office offer a mountain forecast specifically for the Exmoor National Park.

Navigation: Don't rely on mobile apps for navigation. WiFi and mobile phone coverage is patchy across some areas of Exmoor. Always have with you a detailed map, such as an Ordnance Survey map (OL9 covers Exmoor), a torch, spare batteries for your torch and a compass. A red light torch is recommended if you would like to see what you're doing and want to preserve your night vision.

Gear: Walking boots are highly recommended at all locations. They give more ankle support than shoes. Always have warm weather clothes with you. Having several light layers rather than one big heavy coat is recommended as you can better adjust layers to suit the conditions. Hats, scarves and gloves are essential for winter stargazing. A whistle is useful for communication when there is no mobile phone signal.

Public Rights of Way: Keep to public rights of way. All 15 Exmoor stargazing sites are on public access land.

Timing: Let someone know where you're going and what time you'll likely be back. That way if you do get lost or something happens any rescue party will know where to find you!

WHEN YOU'RE OUT and about over Exmoor at night you'll probably hear sounds or experience sights that you're unfamiliar with. Whether it's scuffling in the undergrowth, the call of a night bird in flight or a sudden flashing shadow across the Moon, this quick identifier guide will help you work out what you've just seen or heard in the night air.

Nightjar

Nocturnal summer visitor from Africa.
When to See / Hear: Summer nights.
Habitat: Exmoor's heathlands and bracken.
Night Behaviour: Male's churring call at night. Seen hawking for food at dusk and dawn. Silhouetted against a light source Nightjars look like the shape of a kestrel.

Opposite:
Nocturnal migrating birds.
F Decomite

Nightjar.
Dûrzan cîrano

Badgers

Badgers are widespread residents on Exmoor.

When to See / Hear: All year round.

Habitat: Badger setts are found in Exmoor's woodlands and hedgerows.

Night Behaviour: Badgers forage for food at night. Easiest seen during short summer nights. Look for fresh earth-piling activity outside badger sett entrances. Sometimes badger footprints can be seen in any soft mud nearby.

Badger.

Red Deer on Exmoor.
John Shortland

Red Deer

Red deer have existed on Exmoor since prehistoric times. Currently Exmoor's red deer population numbers 3,000.
When to See / Hear: All year round.
Where: Areas close to forestry and dense woodland on Exmoor.
Night Behaviour: Red deer are most active at night. They come out from the cover of trees at dusk and can also be seen at dawn. September to November is rutting season. You might get to hear the ferocious roar of the stags during the night. It'll make the hairs on the back of your neck stand up!

Foxes

Fox.
Jan's Canon

Foxes are widespread residents on Exmoor.
When to See / Hear: All year round.
Where: Virtually anywhere around Exmoor. Look out for dens near woodland areas. If you detect a sharp musky smell the den is likely to be active.
Night Behaviour: Foxes are opportunists and will forage for all kinds of food scraps. If you're near a food source you might get to see them.

Barn Owl.
Peter Trimming

Barbastelle Bat.

Barn Owls

Britain's most loved owl is found on Exmoor.
When to See / Hear: All year round.
Where: Meadows, river banks and rough pasture around Exmoor, especially those close to barns and derelict buildings.
Night Behaviour: Barn owls are seen swooping across their hunting grounds at dusk and dawn. They are most active at night, and can be heard to occasionally hiss as they defend their territory.

Barbastelle Bats

Exmoor is home to one of only a few maternity roosts of this nationally rare bat
When to See / Hear: April to October.
Where: Exmoor's oak woodlands.
Night Behaviour: Barbastelle bats hunt from dusk until dawn, feeding on moths, midges and other night insects. Use a bat detector set to 32KHz to detect their calls. Another 14 species of bat are also present on Exmoor.

Moths

Oak Eggar Moth.
Entomart

There are more than 1200 species of moth living on Exmoor. These include the Emperor, Oak Eggar and Yellow Underwing, all of which rely on Exmoor's heath plants as a source of food for their caterpillars.
When to See / Hear: Spring until autumn.
Where: All over Exmoor. Many moths have particular habitats. The Scarce Blackneck for example is only found along Exmoor's rocky coastal slopes.
Night Behaviour: Many moth species are attracted to light. Use a torch or lantern in the summertime to bring them to you.

Hedgehogs are active across Exmoor in the late spring, summer and autumn.

When to See / Hear: April to October

Where: Found all over Exmoor along hedgerows and in woodland

Night Behaviour: Hedgehogs forage for food at night. You'll often hear them first, scuffling in amongst leaves and undergrowth near hedgerows and woodland. Sometimes a soft scamper over the ground can be heard when they move quickly.

Hedgehog.
Gaudete

Dormouse.
Danielle Schwarz

Dormice

Exmoor's ancient woodlands are a great place to find the elusive dormouse.

When to See / Hear: Summer and autumn.

Where: In the branches of trees and shrubs in woodland.

Night Behaviour: Dormice are active at night, feeding on nuts, berries and insects. They spend much of their time several metres off the ground, and they are very quiet so it is a challenge to see or hear them.

Migrating Birds

Songbirds like warblers, thrushes, buntings, woodcocks, blackbirds and swallows migrate at night.

When: Spring and autumn.

Where: In the sky over Exmoor.

Night Behaviour: Many migrating songbirds choose to fly at night. Some make their journey in a single powered flight, while others will stop to feed. Look and listen for them during spring and autumn when the weather patterns favour migration over South West Britain. One of the best ways to look for them is to watch the Moon through a telescope using a low power eyepiece. If you're lucky you might catch bird flocks silhouetted in the Moon's light.